Three Plays
by Christina
Anderson

Print edition.
ISBN: 978-1-7341402-7-9

stripwireharlot.com.

TABLE OF CONTENTS

Acknowledgements

Much appreciation and gratitude to all my theater and playwriting teachers over the years. In particular: Paula Zieg, Paula Vogel, Elmo Terry-Morgan, and Lynn Nottage. Many thanks to all the wonderful actors, directors, stage managers, interns, fellows, and designers who've been a part of my productions, workshops, and readings. Thank you to Sarah, Sheila, and Jackie for making this collection possible. To my mom and aunt, thank you for all the ways you supported me doing this wacky thing called playwriting. And to Kari, thank you for your love. It reminds this eternal dramatist to close the laptop, look up, and breathe in the beauty of this world.

My writing practice is a process.
A process of letting go and holding on.
A finished play is often linked to the beginning of a new one.
I begin again (and again) (and again) …
I finish again (and again) (and again) …

My body of work holds
every play I've written
every play I will write
and
every play I probably won't get the chance to write.
I practice abundance within my voice, within the work.

I breathe into questions. (That's usually how I start.)
I follow with curiosity
which creates an openness and allows possibility.

Why is 'x' this way?
How did it get that way?
What if it were something different?

These questions motivate the work.

And then I read, watch, listen.
I investigate. Research. Ideas already discussed.
Expressions already created.
And from curiosity a world appears. Characters form.
They speak desires, expose faults—they map their existence.
I watch, listen. Build. Construct.

My intention is my certainty.
Each play pulsates. I know this because
I instill my vigor into each one.
I challenge and surprise myself

…in turn
…ments surprise and challenge my audience.
…ch play has a spark of joy, a playfulness.
…ch one celebrates live performance. An opportunity to
…alive and experience an ephemeral moment with others.

…aim my right to exist in America. In the theatre.
…laim a right for my characters and their stories to exist.
…write plays is to create community.
…ild great.
…eam big.
…ay worlds soar past the lights, through the roof, and embrace
…e universe.
…nd, yet, the characters remain close to you, to me, to us.
…e connect to each other among our own baggage, insecurities,
…sumptions.
…a my plays there's always a chance to connect.

…ou're
…illing.

…he plays teach me as I build them.
…hey are my chance to tell a good story.
…o speak a truth.
…each deep into histories and layer visions.

…his collection contains three of my plays.
…ach one represents a personal awakening in my craft.

Good Goods came from a Paula Vogel "bakeoff" prompt.
The theme was possession.
And I had recently read William Inge's play *Bus Stop*,
which sparked an obsession with the power of entrances and exits.
And … the challenge to use a single set with full intention and
purpose.

This play also sparked my curiosity with time and theatricality.
Can I have multiple time periods exist all at once
in this fictitious southern town?

The year I lived in The Bay inspired *How to Catch Creation*.
Again, I was curious about the impact of time …
how it moves relationships, creates space and connection.
I wanted to write dynamic, loving,
complicated Black queer women. The women who I discovered,
admired, adored, and loved while in The Bay.

And I wanted to show Black love in all its forms:
friendship, found family, heart-to-heart, body-to-body, art form-
art form.

The third play, *hollow roots*, marks the beginning of my fascinati
with Black women and direct address. I read Wallace Shawn's *Grasses
a Thousand Colors*.
And was inspired by the vivid world-building while also witnessing
a character's transformative journey.

I started writing *hollow roots* when Barack Obama had just been electe
president and I kept reading and hearing white folks say his victo
marked the beginning of a "post-race" society.
I didn't know any people of color who felt that way.
But I wondered … what would it look like if a Black woman becam
"raceless" right before our eyes?
Can she transform into a "neutral" being from the inside out?

And finally, one quick glossary note …

I started using the "=.=" symbol in my plays over twenty years ago.
At the time I knew there were pauses in the dialogue that specific
characters owned.

silences were never dangling in the air. Someone on stage had
session of it, even if only for a moment.

hat symbol became a visual marker of who held the silence.

dn't have a name for this symbol back then. Daniel Banks (theater
ctor, my collaborator and friend) referred to them as "chicken
:" so the name stuck.

"=.=" are chicken feet.
eat that's the duration of a sneeze.
ven the context of the moment, it can denote a character's gesture,
k, shift.
w do you say "I love you" by picking up a cup?
w do you say "fuck you" by putting a cup down?
can also be the character's decision to say the following line, or to
t say it and choose to say something else.
ometimes write the chicken feet intention in parenthesis.
ther times I won't.
=

hank you for reading these plays.
nd taking the time to live in these worlds and hang out with these
aracters.

- Christina Anderson, Berkeley 2022

Good Goods:
to have, to hold,
to set loose your soul

<u>Players:</u>

Stacey – Black American male. 28 years old. The former straight in a comedy duo with Patricia. Now he's inherited his father's gen. store called Good Goods.

Truth – Black American male. 35 years old. The shop assistant an watch guard of Good Goods.

Wire (aka Patrick) – Black American male. 30 years old. A messenger. Short in stature.

Patricia (aka Patty) – Black American female. 29 turning 30 years Wire's twin sister. Also the other half of the comedy duo.

Sunny – Black American female. 18 years old. A young lady who befriends Patricia.

Waymon as Hunter Priestess– Black American male. Ageless.

Factory Folk - Black American male. Middle-aged.

<u>Time:</u>

Swings like a pendulum from 1961 - 1994. It can feel like one year while being in another year. The town's history can change in a second or in several hundred (thousand?) days. Years can happen all once, or one at a time. Time is relative and always moving. Have fur with it.

<u>Place:</u>

The side pocket of America. It's a small, unknown city / county / town / village that doesn't appear on any map. You have to know about it to get to it. And even then you have to know somebody who from there to survive.

This is what we see:

A panoramic view of the Good Goods shop and connecting room.

Starting from stage right we see 2 or 3 steps that lead to a back porch that leads to a back door that takes us to a cramped room that functions as the bedroom/kitchen/dining room/study of Stacey Good.

This room leads to a curtain that takes us to the Good Goods shop. The shop leads to the front door that takes us to the front porch that leads to 2 or 3 steps that takes us offstage.

The shelves in Good Goods are stocked with various products: cans of this stuff; bottles of that; sacks; boxes big & small; pots-n-pans; candy bins, etc. Modern items are mixed with antiquated ones [e.g. a neon sign on a wall, kerosene lamps line the shelf underneath it]. Two medium-sized boxes are on the front porch.

The sky behind the Good Goods establishment is grey. The air is wet.

A large brick building can be seen in the distance. Some windows are covered with stained glass, others with slats of wood.

The battered façade makes it diffic⋯
determine the building's function. ⋯
signs or markings identify its purpo⋯
The only indication that the buildi⋯
operational is the blue smoke that
squirms from its pipes.

The sun attempts to break the grey ⋯
light the morning.

The sound of the building's whistle
signals the start of a workday. The c⋯
is faint, but the presence of labor loo⋯
over the shop.

Stacey enters stage right, carrying a
couple of shirts and pants fresh off th⋯
line. He wears an outfit that's made
up of pieces from various suits.

He climbs the steps leading to the bac⋯
porch and enters through the back do⋯
into his bedroom. He dumps his cloth⋯
on the bed. Crosses over to a pile of
tapes and shuffles through a few,
deciding what he wants to listen to. H⋯
picks a cassette and puts it into the ta⋯
deck that hangs above his bed. Presses
play. As the sound plays from the
machine, Stacey starts folding his
clothes.

He folds his shirts, pants in a way tha⋯
indicates he may have worked retail a⋯
some point.

The cassette picks up in the middle of a
comedy routine. It's the voice of a
woman with a raspy voice [think
Moms Mabley or Whoopie Goldberg]

Voice from the tape player:

:kle] / Yea, like the other night / I'm goin through the channels / it's late
ight / I already put my man to sleep / you know what I'm saying ladies /
:ghter] / I can't go to sleep after I get down / you know? / I'm ready to
-BoP / but my man turns into Stepin Fetchit / just passes OUT /
ghter, applause] / So I'm up late at night after my … escapades [*chuckle*] /
I'm clicking through the channels / and I stop at this movie / it's called
<u>Devil Doll</u> / [*the solo clap of recognition from an audience member*] / aw,
mutha-fucka, I know what you into if you clapping for this freaky shit /
:ghter] / you can always tell who into what when they clap / " you notice
v the smell of ass never really leaves your fingers?" / [*sounds of the
:edienne clapping enthusiastically, followed by an eruption of laughter from the
:lience*] / [*comedienne chuckles*] / just clap, don't care what I'm bout to say
:t …

> *Truth, the watch guard and shop assistant,
> steps up on the front porch. A worn backpack
> is strapped to his back. He has a key to the
> front door, unlocks it. Turns on the lights in
> the store. Stacey checks his watch, knowing
> its Truth. The men don't speak. Stacey
> continues to fold. Truth removes his
> backpack, gets settled. He crosses to the safe,
> spins the dial three times, stopping at each
> number in the password. He opens the safe
> and pulls out the till for the register, counts
> the bills as:*

Voice from the tape player:

evil Doll is about this crazy ass hypnotist-voodoo-ventriloquist-man/ who
as this dummy / straight up 3 foot tall dummy that he props up on his lap
nd does the / "what do ya say, Mack?" kind of jokes / and then he tells this
ummy to walk around / and the dummy hops off his lap and just struts
round / [*does a gesture we can't see, audience on tape laughs*] / I'm like what the
ell is this?? Come to find out he den up and put somebody's soul in the
amn doll—

> *Stacey shuts off the tape.*
>
> *He puts his clothes away in a cardboard box
> and slides it under the cot. He exits his
> bedroom, enters the shop.*

Truth: Hey, hey now.
Stacey: Hey now.

*Truth finishes counting the cash. Then
he places each stack of bills in its right
place in the drawer. Shuts it.*

Truth: What you know about?
Stacey: Nuthin much. What's on with you?
Truth: Day in. Day out. You know.
Stacey: I hear that …
Truth: Who's that you listenin to?
Stacey: Wire got it for me.
Truth: Sounds funny.
Stacey: Not yet. We'll see. She's from out east. She's young. 19, 20 …?
Truth: Is she cute?
Stacey: With a mouth like that?
Truth: It's an act.
Stacey: She's pretty. Not for you though.
Truth: How you know what's for me?
Stacey: She can <u>see</u> that's how I know. One look at you and she'd burn
outta here with the quickness.
Truth: Pssshh. She ain't goin no where. This [*re: his body*] is handcrafted,
prime cut, one-of-a-kind—
Stacey: … assembly-line, off-brand, second-hand, patch-work—
Truth: Leave <u>your</u> goods out of it—
Stacey: You wanna talk all that junk while you bringin in them boxes on
the front porch?
Truth [*sarcastic*]**:** It would be my pleasure. Boss.

*Stacey has a slight reaction to being
called "boss" in such a sarcastic tone, but
he covers it.*

*Truth exits the shop to the front porch.
He grabs a box brings it in as:*

Truth: What's in these?
Stacey: Special orders. The Factory Folk asked for some things.
Truth: They get some change in they pockets …

ey: And come straight here. Cain't be mad at that.

th: I shouldn't be …

Truth crosses back onto the front porch.
Looks up:

th: Might rain.

cey [*from inside the shop*]: *It always looks like rain.*

th: But I smell it. Wire was sayin it was rainin something awful over
    yonder. Rain travels.

cey: So do lies.

Truth brings in the remaining box.

ith: If it's raining come lunchtime, them Factory Folk gonna have to
    crowd on the front porch to eat. Spill over into the shop.

acey: You sound uneasy about that.

uth: No uneasiness …. It's just hard keep an eye on things when people
    clump together. It's hard to keep track of whose hands been where.

acey: You been worried about they hands before?

uth: No.

acey: So, why you thinkin you need to keep track of hands now?

uth: =.=

       =.=

       'Cause people get ideas when things change.

       A window of opportunity cracks open when responsibility … shifts.

acey: Well, that's why my daddy kept you here, Truth.

       To make sure that window you talkin bout is locked. Tight.

       Plus, those Factory Folk are good people. They wouldn't take nuthin
       from the store. Why you suspectin them?

ruth: Who else comes through here, Stacey?

tacey: You.

ruth: =.=

       =.=

       Well, well, you livin in that back room. You on the suspect list, too.

tacey: I'ma steal from my own store?

ruth: This is your daddy's store.

tacey: Is he here?

ruth: It's still in his name, so it's like he's here.

tacey: But he's not in this shop. On this property. He ran away.

       Skipped out.

Truth: Until the paperwork shifts, you stealing from <u>your daddy's</u> store. This is Mister Good senior's establishment until the papers say otherwise.

Stacey: Who says I'd steal from anywhere?

Truth: Who says I'd steal?

Stacey: =.=

Truth: =.=

Stacey: =.=

Truth: Your daddy didn't call me Truth to make a joke.

Stacey: =.=

Truth: =.=

Stacey: =.=

Truth: If you start suspecting me – If <u>we</u> start suspecting <u>each</u> <u>other</u> ... this shop gonna go outta business in a day.

Stacey: =.=

Truth: =.=

> *Truth starts unpacking a box.*
> *Stacey crosses to the register re-count*
> *the bank.*
>
> *Truth notices this slight, but doesn't*
> *take it in full on. Instead:*

Truth [*under his breath*]: Been here a damn week ...

Stacey [*stops counting*]: What's that?

Truth: I said, you been back a damn week.

Stacey: And?

Truth: And I'm just stating a truth. I been here since I was a lil boy. You been back a week.

Stacey: =.=

Truth: Mm-hm.

Stacey: =.= [*returns to counting*]

Truth: =.= [*unpacks the box*]

Stacey: =.= [*sounds of him handling the bills*]

> *Stacey finishes the count. Returns the*
> *money back in its register.*

Truth: Humph. Second guessing me ...

*Stacey exits the shop, enters his
bedroom. He crosses to the small
writing desk grabs sheets of paper.
Exits the bedroom, enters the shop
then hands the papers to Truth.*

Truth: What's this?

*Wire enters stage left, climbs the front
steps. Puffs on a handmade cigarette.*

Stacey: It's a list of who ordered what. Check off what's in the boxes.
Truth [*reading the list*]: Bunch of junk.
Stacey: =.=
Truth: Magazines, deck of cards, flip books, pocket video games …
     Waste of time.
Stacey: Keeps the shop in business and money in your pocket.
Truth: Yea, yea …
Wire: Hey hey now.

Wire puts out the cigarette. Enters the shop.

Stacey: Hey now.
Truth: Hey hey.
Wire: It's gonna be hot today, y'all.
Stacey: Truth was just talkin bout rain.
Wire: That could happen, too.
     A hot rain.
     There was a horrible storm over in—
Truth: I was just tellin him that. He didn't believe me though.
Wire: It was something awful. Roads washed out. I had to sleep overnight
     in the post office. Hard floors over there. My back ain't actin right
     cause of it. Y'all running smooth 'round here?
Stacey [*quick*]: Yea.
Wire: Truth?
Truth: For now …
Stacey: Truth …
Wire: What's goin down?
Stacey: Nuthin. Nuthin's goin down.
Truth: Not yet.
Stacey [*to Truth*]: Would you stop talkin mess?
Wire: I'd prefer y'all talk sense than mess—

15

Truth: I was sayin we got to be careful since Stacey's daddy left. People think they can get away with liftin goods now.

Wire: Who y'all think would lift from here?

Truth: Stacey claimed it could be me—

Stacey: I was makin a point. Truth said it could be me—

Truth: Cause he don't wanna believe it could be those Factory Folk.

Wire: Why would they lift from here?

Stacey: That's what I'm sayin, Wire.

Wire: They all glad to be workin … pays more than liftin merchandise.

Truth: Most of them fools don't know left from right, back from front since they started workin in that factory.

Truth These days "easy" is more appealing than "backbreakin." And this store is an easy lift.

Wire: You slippin on your job, Truth?

Truth: I ain't slippin on nuthin. It's the new management.

Stacey: Here we go ….

Truth: Mr. Good senior had a certain posture about him. Stacey is …

Wire [*benefit of the doubt*]: Figurin things out. Getting used to running a business.

Truth: Settlin in has its moments of … ignorance, you see?

Stacey [*to Truth*]: He know I cain't fire him. That's why he's talkin like this.

Wire: Who made that rule?

Truth: It's in the papers. If Stacey fires me, I can go to the mayor and report his ass. Mr. Good senior got a clause in there that says gettin rid of me puts the property tax on a sliding scale. However much profit the store makes in a given month, Stacey got to give it all to the city.

Stacey: I'd break even all the damn time. Won't ever have extra cash. I got to keep him around, or I don't make money for myself. So he talks all kinds of shit, because he knows I cain't kick him out.

Truth: Why would you get rid of the only somebody who knows how this shop works? Woulda collapsed the first day if it wasn't for me …

Stacey: I been in 4 razor fights, spent 2 nights in a white man's trunk, and made love with a blind man, if I ain't collapsed during all that, I ain't gonna collapse running my daddy's shop—

Truth: First mistake, Wire: taking special orders.

Stacey: Second mistake: not reading the fine print on them damn papers.

Truth: He needs glasses, too.

Stacey: I need some slack is what I need—

Wire: Y'all serving breakfast?

th: =.=

=.=

Technically: we ain't open.

re: But the door's never closed to guests, right?

cey: You more than a guest, Wire. Help yourself.

> *Wire slaps a few bills on the counter as payment. He makes himself a bowl of cereal.*

cey: You don't have to pay, Wire—

> *Truth rings it up. Tucks the money in the register.*

uth: Thank you. Have a nice day.

acey: Truth—

ire: It's alright, Stacey.

> *Truth crosses back to the boxes. He sorts through goods.*

> *Stacey exits the shop, enters his bedroom. He sits at the small writing desk. Does paper work.*

Wire: =.= [*chewing, spoon clanks against bowl*]

Truth: =.= [*sorting*]

Stacey: =.= [*reading, shuffling papers*]

Wire [*to Truth*]: I was up in that factory the other day.

Truth: Yea?

Wire: Yea. Had to deliver a message. The building itself is grimy as hell: rusty stairs, dank hallways. Ain't too surprised by the condition of it though. That building is older than me. And I'm 29 … 30. I'm 30. That's right.

=.=

=.= [*waiting for them to acknowledge it's his birthday. No luck.*]

And you older than me, Truth. And that building was here before you.

Truth [*concentrating on sorting*]: Nobody took care of it over the years, Wire.

Wire: Now, I imagine if I didn't take care of myself for 29 … 30 years. I'd be a sack funk and confusion. Mm-hm. So, it makes sense that building is as pitiful as it is …

Wire realizes no one remembers his birth...
He's disappointed by this and continues th...
small talk to cover his emotions.

Wire: … but the equipment they put in there is nice.
Brand new and <u>expensive</u>. Them Factory Folk got to wash they're hands <u>before</u> they go on the floor. They all uppity about it, too.

Mention of the factory animates Truth:

Truth: I don't understand what they got to be uppity about.
Operatin the machines ain't nuthin compared to ownin em.
Wire: Cain't get down on em for doin they job.
Truth: Every last one of them jobs is a sign of defeat—
Wire: I'm not tryin to talk politics, Truth. Just wanna chat. Tellin you what it's like in there, alright?
Truth [*easing up*]: Alright …
Wire: Alright. I had to deliver a message to the foreman from the C.E.O. himself.
Truth: Sayin what?
Wire: Eh, a bunch of numbers. Product such-and-such needs a reduction of blah-de-blah to double the intake of uh-huh-yea-yea. But I couldn't get over those machines. That building is a prime example o sheep's clothing.
Truth: As much history that place has held I'm surprised they even decided to reuse it.
Wire: What you meanin?
Truth: I mean buildings got rings in em just like a tree trunk.
Got a history like me and you.
Wire: So.
Truth: So, I'm surprised given that building's heavy history they still went ahead and turned it into a pencil factory.
Wire: What heavy history? It used to be a high school, a prison, a hospital, a nightclub, an outlet store, a haunted house during October, a mega church, and a smack pad … shit, you reuse your drawers just as many times before you wash em and Mister Good still used you—

Stacey, hearing Wire's comment,
laughs.

Truth [*ignoring Stacey*]: Wire, I ain't talkin about none of that.
Wire [*to Stacey*]: You like that?

ey: That was good.

h: What. I'm. Saying. Is …

Stacey and Wire calm down.

th: … Ivory saw a prophecy in that building.

e: That's the heavy history you talkin bout?
You think they care about some brown gurl's vision?
Makin money is about makin money. No matter what history is holdin.

Stacey exits his bedroom, enters the shop.

cey: What brown gurl? What prophecy?

re: The brown gurl is Ivory Evans.

th: And she was standin in that building when she saw her people's demise.

ire: Wandered inside between its reincarnations.

cey [*to Wire*]: Why don't I know about this?

th [*interjection*]: It's something you had to be here to know about.

ire: None of us was even born when it happened, Truth.
You know about it, Stacey.
There's that song people sing about Ivory.
"Brown Ivory Tears."

acey: "Brown Ivory Tears"…? I thought that was just some ol' town song.

uth: Based on a true story …

Vire [*sings*]: Ivory, my Ivory, coastin 'long the sea.
Ivory, my Ivory, wonderin who she'll be.
The sun behind her.
The grass below.
She walked until she walked no more ….

ruth [*sings*]: A mama calls …
A daddy calls …
A brother calls …
A sister calls …
And the devil answered in Ivory tears.
Brown Ivory's red, red tears.

Stacey [*sings*]: Ivory stopped and fell to her knees.
She saw her people pulled a part like weeds.
The heavens behind her.
The hells below.
She screamed until she screamed no more.

19

Stacey *(cont'd):*

    =.=

    [*speaks*] That's a true story?

Truth: Happened right in that building.

    She saw her whole legacy, past present and future, wiped out.

    Family claim she saw all these brown faces smiling at her, then wi
the wave of a hand death took 'em just like that.

    She screamed so loud the whole town heard her.

    The family scooped her up, carried her back to the house.

    She kept hollerin and hollerin about the prophecy. 'til she
died later that night.

Blue smoke shoots from the factory
pipes.

Wire: That family still ain't right because of it.

    Keep mostly to themselves. They a bit off, ain't they Truth?

Truth: Something ain't right in em.

Wire: The whole family, cousins sons daughters mamas daddies grands
and greats, all came back.

    They live on the other side of the factory. A handful of miles to the
north of it.

Stacey: They stay locked up in their houses?

Wire: Well, they need money, food, clothes.

    They got to get out to gather those things.

    I got caught up in a conversation with one of the boys a while back.

    Bumped into him a few towns over. He came over all excited to see
familiar face.

    And I'm thinkin, "ain't nuthin familiar 'bout you."

    But he let on who he was.

    Tells me he keeps a picture of Ivory on him at all times. Said the
whole family does.

    Girls got lockets around their necks, the boys got her sewn into thei
caps.

    That's the only way they feel safe when they leave the house.

Stacey: Why would anybody wanna carry Armageddon on their body?

Wire: They thinkin Ivory is a shield more than a reaper.

Truth: Mm-hm. And now all the men in this town are in there whittlin
blocks of wood. The women are packin em in crates.

    15 hours a day for $2 an hour and they got nerve enough to be
uppity.

Stacey: Two dollars?

Wire: Minimum wage dropped again a few months back.

uth: [*to Wire*] High-baller missed the goings-on of the everyday
citizen. [*to Stacey*] You see why your daddy didn't do special orders?
Hard earned money on junk.

cey: They got a right to spend their money however they want to.

uth: Drug dealers talk the same trash, don't they—

ire [*mediating*]: All these stories about prophecies and grim reapin
creeps me <u>out</u>. Don't it creep you out, Stacey?

acey: =.=

ire: Truth?

uth: =.=

ire: If I get any request to deliver a message on the other side of that
factory, I make sure I carry as much protection as possible.

acey: =.=
Like what?

ire: I got a friend who's a librarian.
He wrote out armor scriptures from every religious text he could get
his hands on.
Said to me, "Wire, I know you travel all over and sometimes you have
to tell people what they don't wanna hear. You need protection from
the danger that can fall in your path." I keep it right here:

> *Wire lifts up his shirt. A sheet of paper,
> yellow from age, is wrapped in plastic and
> taped to his chest. Words are scribbled on it in
> blue ink.*
>
> *Stacey leans in to get a closer look. There's a
> lingering.*
>
> *Truth declines.*

Wire: I had my mama and my daddy lay hands on it. Every six months, I
take it to the spot where I saw somebody die for the first time.

Stacey: And where was that?

Wire: Out in front of Lonnie's joint.
Two men got into it. One of em had a knife. The other didn't see it
comin.
I walk over there and stand where that man took his last breath.

Truth: That's awful, Wire. I didn't know you do that.

> *Wire winces at this judgment and pulls his
> shirt down. Tucks it back in his pants. Stacey
> steps back.*

Wire: A lot of things you don't know, Truth.

Stacey: Amen to <u>that</u>.

Truth: Why y'all tag-teamin me?

Wire: I don't like nobody judging my armor.

Truth: I'm not judging.

Wire: Said it was awful.

Truth: That's cause it is.

Wire: Being a messenger's a hard job. Especially for somebody my size.
    Need all the help I can get.

Truth: I understand that, Wire. I got you your job. I know what it entails.

Wire: Well then don't call how I do things "awful".

Truth: Alright.

Truth returns to the goods.

Wire finishes his cereal.

Stacey exits the shop, enters his bedroo

Wire: =.= [*chewing. spoon clanking against bowl*]

Truth: =.= [*sorting goods*]

Stacey: =.= [*reading, shuffling papers*]

Wire slurps the remaining milk from his bowl, gets up, goes into the Stacey's room. Closes the curtain that functions as Stacey's door.

Truth sees this out the corner of his eye but says nothing.

Stacey knows Wire has entered his room, but says nothing.

Wire sits on Stacey's bed. Stacey sits at a small table going over papers.

Wire: =.= [*breathing*]

Truth: =.= [*sorting*]

Stacey: =.= [*reading*]

Wire stretches out across Stacey's bed in a familiar way. Breathes. Rubs his chest / armor. The plastic that

surrounds his armor crinkles. Wire
stares at the ceiling.

Truth looks to the curtain. He rises to
his feet. Crosses over to the front door.
Steps out to the porch. Sits on the stairs.
Smokes a cigarette.

re: Truth act like he don't believe in anything.

cey: He believes in the truth. My daddy gave him that name for a
reason.

ire: More than one kind of truth. The way he think is narrow.

acey: =.=

ire: =.=

acey: =.=

ire: It's my birthday today. Did you know that?

acey: I didn't. I didn't know that. Happy birthday, Wire.

ire: I figured you didn't. You woulda said something by now. I was tryin
to hint at it earlier.

acey: I figured it was tomorrow since Patty's—

ire [*quick*]: She was born after midnight. I was born before. That's why
we have it on different days. Even though we're twins.

acey: Mhm.

ire: Our folks would switch the day we'd have a party every year.
But ever since Patty left. It's usually just my party.

tacey: You have a party every year?

Wire: Yea. But I'm usually delivering a message somewhere. So I walk
into a bar and just order a shot for myself. Tell the bartender it's my
birthday and ask him if he'll plug in my player so I can hear KoKo
Taylor's "Wang Dang Doodle." You know that song?

tacey: Yea, yea. I know that song. I heard her sing it live.

Wire [*sits up*]: You did?

Stacey: I did. I was on the road. Got invited to a party and she showed up.
Started jamming with the band.

Wire: Oh, wow …

Stacey sings the chorus to "Wang Dang
Doodle." Wire joins for the last line. Then:

Stacey: Yea, man, Wire. I ain't never gonna forget that. It was a small
joint, you know? People dancing like they under water. Blue smoke.
Red lights. She didn't have a mic or nothin was just singing, singing
from here.

Stacey taps Wire's chest / armor. Plastic crinkles.

Wire touches his own chest just as Stacey removes his hand.

Stacey: I left outta there with the sunrise. Bright orange. Hanging like a big piece of fruit from a tree.

Wire: That ain't nuthin like a party I ever have.

Stacey: I smoked some of the best grinds of my life that night.
You ever get goose bumps?

Wire: Yea.

Stacey: Yea. All over, you know?

Wire: Yea.

Stacey: Uh-huh. Everybody was dancing.

Wire: Dancing ….

Stacey: And we had a really good show that night. Patty and me. We tore the house down. Had everybody crackin up, laughing. And some nights, when we did a good show, I'd be so down afterwards but th was one of the few times I kept a buzz all night. The goose bumps, the blue smoke …

Wire: =.=

Stacey: =.=

Wire: =.= [*lays back on the bed*]

Stacey: =.= [*looks at Wire across his bed*]
=.= [*a consideration*]
=.= [*slowly turns back to his papers*]

Wire: =.=

Stacey: =.=

Wire: Did you listen to the comedy tape I gave you?

Stacey: I started it.

Wire: I think she's pretty funny.

Stacey: I haven't listened to it all the way through.

Wire: That <u>Devil Doll</u> bit is funny.
=.=
I thought it was funny.
=.=

Stacey [*turning back to Wire*]: We should have a party for you.

Wire [*sits up*]: For me?

Stacey: Yea. You got any deliveries you gotta make tonight?
I'll throw you a party.

Wire: Really?

Stacey: Really.

e [*remembering ...*]: Damn.

cey: What?

> *Wire retrieves a small date book from his pocket. Flips through it.*

re: I gotta deliver a message to a worker in the mines.

cey: Do it now.

re: I cain't.

cey: Why not?

ire: I gotta wait for his woman to have the baby.
  Gotta tell the father if it's a boy or a girl.

cey: Oh. Well, we can have it later. Or earlier. Whenever you want it.

ire: Who we gonna invite?

> *Just as Wire asks this question, Patricia steps up on the front porch. Truth stands up, the cigarette hanging from his mouth. She stands face to face with Truth.*

tricia: Hey now.

uth: =.= [*speechless*]

tricia: Hey now, Truth.

ruth: ... hey hey now ... Patricia.

tricia: Aw, now, we know each other better than that. You call me Patty
  if I call you Truth, hear? What's good with you? What's good
  around here?

ruth: What, what you doin back?

atricia: Mr. Good senior took the hospitality with him when he jetted
  out of town?

> *Patricia holds out her cheek. Truth removes the cigarette from his mouth, leans in and kisses Patricia on the cheek.*

Patricia [*re: the cigarette*]: You got another one for me?

> *Truth gives Patricia a cigarette. He lights it for her. She puffs.*

Patricia: Stacey around?

Truth: Uhhh, yea.

Patricia: How's he managin things?

Truth: It's been a week ...

Patricia: You can destroy lives in a week, Truth.

Truth: There's a lot to pick up. A lot to learn.

Patricia: You helpin him?

Truth: I have to. If he sinks this store, I'ma have to work at the factory.

Patricia: What factory?

Truth: Over yonder.

> *Truth points to the factory in the distance*
> *Blue smoke fills the sky above it.*

Patricia: What is that?

Truth: That's what happens when we lose and they win. 'stead of markin their territory with flags, they got folks elbow to elbow in there makin pencils.

Patricia: =.= [*looking at the building*]

Yea, I see why you'd wanna stay workin here.

Truth: Stacey's doin alright. Cain't tell him that though or else he'll get lazy.

=.=

How you keepin?

Cain't be too good if you showin up here seven days after he left yc

Patricia: I'm doin fine. .

Has he said anything to you about how he left things with me?

Truth: No. But he and I don't really talk like that.

I imagine he just walked out.

Patricia: You got a pretty dull imagination.

Truth: Patty, I didn't want to bother him. Disrupt y'all. But I had to.

Patricia: You had to?

Truth: He's in the papers.

Patricia: We know how you hold on to them damn documents, Truth.

> *Patricia puts out her cigarette.*
> *She enters the shop, the click of her heels*
> *cause both Wire and Stacey to stand up*
> *They both know that walk.*
>
> *Patricia looks around.*

Patricia: Ain't much changed in here.

> *Stacey exits the bedroom, enters the*
> *shop. Patricia turns to look at him.*

Stacey: Patty.

Patricia: Stacey.

Stacey: =.=

Patricia: =.=

Stacey: =.=

Wire exits the bedroom, enters the shop.

Patricia: Not much has changed at all …

Wire: Hey now.

Patricia: Hey, hey Patrick.

Wire winces at this name.

Wire: I didn't know you were in town. Not surprised though. Figured it
     wasn't a matter of <u>if</u> but <u>when</u>.

Patricia: =.=

Stacey: You just got into town?

Wire: Ma & pop know you're here?

Patricia: =.=

Stacey: =.=

Patricia: =.=

Truth: We got cereal.

Patricia: I'm not hungry, Truth. But thank you.

Truth: =.=

Patricia: Just stepped off the bus.
     Did you hear that, Stacey? The <u>bus</u>.
     And I tore my last pair of stockings.

Truth: We carry hosiery.

Patricia: Stacey knows my size.

Stacey: =.=

Patricia: =.=

*Stacey crosses over to the hosiery. Picks out
Patricia's size. Puts them on the counter as:*

Patricia: What's good with you, big brotha?

Wire: Most everything.

Patricia: Messaging business treatin you well?

Wire: Yes, Patricia. Uh-huh. It is.
     Especially after that endorsement you made up for me.

Stacey: Endorsement?

Wire: Oh, yea. When y'all last comedy album took off around these parts,
     Patty gave me a line to print in the papers:

Patricia [*putting on her shtick*]: "Poked his head back in and gave me the al'
    clear! I've trusted my twin brother to give me the scoop ever since

Wire: I saw a 70% increase in orders after that ad.
    Rest of my competition fell through the cracks. Every single last or
    of them is working at the pencil factory.

Truth: He had to buy a lil book to keep track of his message requests.

Wire: Got so many I couldn't just keep em in my head anymore.
    Capital County knockin out the phone lines a while back was the
    best thing coulda happened to me.

Patricia: How much I owe you, Stacey?

Truth: Nothin … don't owe us a thing.

Stacey: I'll put it on your tab.

Truth: You don't have to worry about us cashing that in anytime soon,
    Patty. Whatever you want while you're here …

Stacey: You can talk to me, and I'll make sure—

Truth: To ask me to pull it for you. Don't have to bother with the back-
    and-forth, Stacey. She can just talk to me. I'll take care of everything

Patricia: Well, however y'all wanna handle it let me know.

> *Sunny steps up on the back porch. She*
> *carries a package wrapped in brown*
> *paper. Raps on the frame of the door.*

Stacey: Who could that be knockin from the back?

Patricia: It might be my guest. Sunny?!

Sunny [*from the back porch*]: Yes, Ms. Patricia?

Patricia: Come on through.

> *Sunny politely steps into Stacey's room.*
> *She looks around the cramped space.*
> *Stacey pulls back the curtain. Sunny*
> *enters the shop. Big smiles. A gap*
> *between her two front teeth. Truth*
> *falls in love the moment he sees her.*
> *Patricia lights up, too, and we see her*
> *blazing charm.*

Patricia: Sunny!

Sunny: I got a lil' turned around at the square, but a nice lady pointed me
    the right way. I said, "I'm looking for the Good Goods general store.
    Such a funny name: Good Goods. But I like sayin it. It's easy to
    walk to the beat of that Good Goods / Good Goods / Good
    Goods …

Sunny does a little dance, carrying the package.

The room watches this little glowing ball of brown beauty. Sunny stops dancing, slightly winded. She returns the gaze of the room. Smiles. Gap.

Sunny: Hello, y'all.

Patricia: Gentlemen, this is Sunny. Sunny this is Stacey—

Sunny: So nice to meet you, Mr—

Stacey: Stacey is fine. The first name is enough.

Sunny: My daddy has all your albums. He'd always say lines from the "Stacey & Patty Got to Keep It Real!" cd.

Stacey: That was a while ago.

Patricia: Not that long ago.
Sunny and I got a hold of each other in the most coincidental way. Life is so funny like that.

Sunny: It is.

Patricia: I had to transfer buses and the only seat available was up front next to Sunny. We got to talkin and well, ten hours later I talked her into comin here with me.

Sunny: I hadn't heard of y'all town before. It was all new to me. And if I have a choice of something familiar or something unknown, I choose the unknown one every time.

Truth: Where you comin from, Sunny?

Sunny: My mama's house.

Stacey: And where is that?

Sunny [*evasive*]: About a five-day bus ride from here.

Stacey: =.=

Truth: =.=

Sunny: It's boring. All crazy boring where I come from, but y'all place is nice. Here. Right now. This shop. These people.
I know Black folks live everywhere, but the way Patricia talked about it here ... knew it was something I ain't never seen before.

Truth [*shucks*]: It's not all that ...

Sunny: You thinkin that cause you familiar with it. All new to me. Patricia extended her hospitality. And she's been a ... fine companion so far. I mean, I know three more people than I did when I got here. [*Smiles. Gap. Truth swoons.*]

Stacey: Where were you headed originally?

Sunny: About a seven-hour bus ride from here.

Stacey: =.=

Truth: I've been up that way.

But it's much nicer here. I think. You'll see prettier things here. I'm glad Patricia got you to take a lil tour of our town.

Sunny: City.

Stacey: What?

Patricia: That's what the welcome sign calls it.

You're officially living in a city, Stacey. You are the owner of the city's Good Goods.

On command, Sunny does a baby jig. The room watches her.

Sunny [*as she dances*]: I wasn't rushing to get where I was going. So I decided to come through.

Truth [*watching her body move*]: Well allll-right.

Sunny stops her jig. Turns to Truth.

Truth [*to Sunny*]: Hey hey now. Hi there. We haven't really met each other yet.

Sunny: Hi.

Patricia: This is Truth.

Sunny: Truth?

Truth: That's what I go by 'round here. Can I take that package for you?

Sunny: Actually, it's for the birthday boy ....

She spins around to Wire.

Sunny: You got to be Patrick!

Sunny holds out the package.

Wire: I am ... But they call me Wire 'round here.

Sunny: =.= [*holding out the package*]

=.= [*holding*]

Lotta people avoidin they birthnames 'round here.

Wire takes the package.

Wire [*to Patricia*]: You got me a gift?

icia: Well, I mentioned to Sunny I was coming down here to celebrate your birthday—well, _our_ birthday—and she came up with the perfect gift. I had a few thoughts but Sunny was kind enough to attend to the details.

ıny: I'm sorry it took me so long. That's always the deal with being a stranger in a friendly town. Small talk on the streets, small talk in the shop, at the register. I asked someone the time, realized I was runnin late and bolted over here.

re: Well ever since the invasion folks around here like to know who's who and what's what.

ıny: Invasion?

ricia [_quick_]: Sunny, it's fine that you were runnin a lil behind. We were all just … standing around …. shooting the rind.

cey [_backhanded_]: The shit and the rind.

tricia: =.=

cey: =.=

nny [_breaks out in the laughter_]: Y'all two are so funny together!

uth: Sunny, are you hungry? We got some cold cereal.

nny: Oh! That would be lovely. I'm pretty hungry. Patricia shared half her roast beef sandwich with me some time last night, but other than that … Thank you, Mr. …

uth: Truth. Nothing before or after, please. Just Truth.

> _As Truth escorts Sunny to a seat and fixes_
> _her a bowl of cereal:_

ınny: I like that. You must've done something incredible to earn that name. Even more incredible to keep it.

ruth: Well, it's a name you have to earn. That's for sure.

Vire [_to Patricia_]: You came all the way here for my—_our_—birthday?

atricia: You sound surprised.

Vire: I am.

atricia: Why?

Vire: For real?

atricia: =.=

Vire: We haven't celebrated together since we were young. You left right after our 20th birthday. Ain't got a card or present until now. 'til Stacey come back here—

Patricia: I'll admit we haven't seen each other—

Wire: Had our birthday together …

Patricia: … I know it's been a minute, but the important thing is we're here now. I mean, it's about the <u>next gig</u> not the one we just finished, ain't that right Stacey?

Wire: =.=

Patricia: Oh, cain't talk to him about the past. Can we?

Stacey: =.=

Stacey turns, goes back to his room:

Patricia: Oh, oh, now Stacey come on …

        [*to Wire*] He's put on some weight, ain't he? In the waist.

Wire: Where you stayin, Patricia?

Patricia: I'ma get me and Sunny a room.

Wire: You don't wanna stay with ma & pa?

Patricia: You still livin there?

Wire: I sleep there. Don't live there.

Patricia: Well I'd like to sleep somewhere else. I don't have answers for all their questions. Not yet.

Wire: You should go by.

Patricia: I will. I will. I'll let em think I'm strutting around overseas a lil while longer. Did they ask about me with Stacey comin back?

Wire: They did. Asked me to ask Stacey what you were doing now that the act is busted.

Patricia winces when she hears the truth said out loud.

Patricia: And what did Stacey tell you to tell them?

Wire: That you had been workin on some solo material. Workin on becoming "the queen of Black comedy."

Patricia: He used that title?

Wire: Yea.

Patricia: =.=

Wire: =.=

Patricia: =.=

Wire: I don't have anything for you, Patty. No birthday present or nuthin.

Patricia: Well, on technical terms my birthday's not until after midnight. So … you got time. [*idea!*] We celebrated our last birthday on my day, so tradition says we have our 30th tonight.

Wire: Tonight?

Patricia: Yea! Were you planning anything?

Wire: Well, Stacey was talking about …

Patricia: Stacey! [*Wire follows holding on to his gift.*] My, my! I just had a
hot idea! We should throw a birthday party! For me and Patrick!
It can be a "welcome home" party for you! And, and a celebration
that Good Goods is still going strong! A big ol' bash.

Stacey: Wire and I were talkin about something chill. Just a lil bitty—

Patricia: Lil bitty?! All these things to celebrate and y'all wanna sit on the
back porch and drink whiskey out of jars?? Uh-uh. No, no. We are
throwing down! Oh! And we can do something from our act,
Stacey! [*Patricia snaps her fingers. Sways to the beat*]
Something light and easy.
Those pencil shavers look for a good time, don't they? Maybe we
can charge a lil' something to cover expenses …

Stacey: That ain't something I wanna do, Patricia.

Patricia: =.=
=.=
You don't' wanna have a good time?
Why?

Stacey: =.=
=.= [*looking for an excuse*]
Been talk about folks planning to lift goods from the store. I don't
wanna throw a big party to give somebody an easy way in.

Patricia: Oh. Well. We can keep it outside. On the porch. Truth can keep
an eye on things. He's been the security man since he was a lil boy.
He can keep an eye on things. We can get someone to sit at the
back porch. We'll perform on the front … it's all easy greasy, my
Stacey.
How about it?
=.=
=.=
=.= [*a giggle from Sunny in the shop with Truth*]

Wire: =.=

Stacey: =.=

Patricia: We'll stop it the moment it gets too rowdy.

Stacey: =.=
=.=
Is this something you wanna do, Wire?

Wire: =.=
=.=
Well, I've spent so many birthdays dancing by myself in a bar …
It'd be nice.

Wire *(cont'd):*
>   If that baby arrives, I'll get somebody to drive me over to tell the
>   daddy. Get there and back here as quick as I can.

Stacey: Alright. A short party.

>   *Patricia is <u>excited</u>. Squeals a little bit.*

Patricia: Sunny and I will take care of everything! Ooooooooo, Patrick
>   this is gonna be a throw down to end all throw downs!

>   *She kisses Wire on the cheek.*
>   *Then kisses Stacey on the lips.*
>   *Runs into the shop.*

Patricia: Sunny! You just about done with your breakfast? We got a party
>   to plan!

Sunny: Ooooooo, a party! Oh that sounds fire! When, where?!

Patricia: Here. Tonight! We're celebrating. Life and … and new
>   beginnings.

Truth [*smiling*]: I like both those things.

Patricia: And our lovely Truth has agreed to keep the peace.

Truth: I have?

Patricia: You have.

Truth: What if I wanna enjoy the party?
>   Who's gonna keep Sunny company—

Sunny: Let's jump to it, Ms Patricia.

>   *The women prepare to go.*
>   *Sunny stops, turns to Truth.*

Sunny: Thank you for the cereal and the talkin, Truth.

>   *Truth just smiles. Unable to speak.*

>   *Green smoke belches from the factory pipes,*
>   *muscling its way past the blue smoke.*

>   *Sunny and Patricia exit stage left.*

>   *The men are left silent.*

>   *Wire sits on Stacey's bed. The gift pressed to*
>   *his chest.*

Stacey sits at his small table, head down.

Truth crosses out the front door and stands on the front porch, staring off in the distance at Sunny and Patricia.

ire: =.=

cey: =.=

uth [*to himself*]: Sho' nuff make Truth holler for relief!

Truth stands for a moment longer. Looks up.

uth: No rain. Not yet. Sunny den chased it away …

He goes back into the shop, returns to special orders.

Wire sits on Stacey's bed.
Truth checks his watch.

ruth [*to Stacey who's in the bedroom*]: This day is movin. That lunch whistle's gonna blow before we know it. What we doin about these orders?

tacey [*duh*]: We'll hand em out.

ruth: I know that, Stacey, but how you wanna to do that?
I don't think we should let 'em all just run up and through here.

tacey: Do whatever you think is right, Truth.

ruth: =.=
=.= [*thinking about it*]
=.=
We should … have em collect out front. Then I'll call out a name. Have the man step forward. Give him his order. And wait for him to step back outside before we call the next name.
They can eat outside. No rain. Sky is still gray. But no rain.

Stacey: Fine, Truth.

Truth sets up the orders.

Wire: =.=

Stacey: =.=

Wire: I need to scrape together a gift for Patty. She got me something. I oughta get her something. Right thing to do.

Stacey: =.=

Wire: Been a while since I had to think of a gift for somebody.

> =.=
>
> =.=
>
> I usually just buy my mama flowers for her days: birthday and mother's day. Buy my daddy smokes for his birthday and father's d
>
> =.=
>
> =.=

Stacey: She ain't gonna care one way or the other.

Wire: Who?

Stacey: Patricia. She ain't gonna care if you get her a gift or not.

Wire: But I do. I care.

Stacey: =.=

Wire: =.= [*thinking what to buy her*]

Stacey: =.=

> *Wire shakes the package it makes a noise.*

Wire: Does that sound expensive to you?

Stacey: You gonna break it, shakin the thing like that.

> *Anxious about that possibility, Wire places* ⸱
> *gently on his lap.*

Wire: =.=

Stacey: I wonder what's the deal with that Sunny gal.

Wire: She makes you wanna look at her.

Stacey: =.=

Wire: Do you know Patty's dress size?

Stacey: [*insert a dress size of the actress playing Patricia here*].

Wire: They'll help me pick a dress out for her at the shop.

Stacey: She ain't gonna want some cheap cotton thing from town.

Wire: =.=

Stacey: =.=

Wire: On our 16th birthday, I bought her gloves.

Stacey [*lost in thought*]: Huh?

Wire: I bought her satin gloves with the fur around the end of em.

Stacey: Oh, yea?

Wire: She bought me some suspenders.

Stacey: =.=

Wire: =.=

Stacey: =.=

Wire: Maybe some nice paper. For writing letters.

Stacey: She don't write letters. She comes up with bits.

e: =.=

   =.=

   A lil notebook then. Like the one I got but bigger.

:ey: She don't write nuthin down cause she thinks folks will steal it.

re: =.=

cey: =.=

re: You keep pissin on my ideas.

cey: Because your ideas are mess buckets, Wire.

re: You ain't helpin none.

cey: Cause Patty ain't gonna care. She's not here to get a gift. She's not here for no birthday.

ire: Well what she here for?

cey: You tellin me you trustin her intentions?

ire: I ain't sayin that.

   I'm returnin her gesture, Stacey. A gift ain't a sign of trust. Ain't a sign of forgiveness. It's just the right thing to do.

cey: =.=

ire: =.=

Wire unwraps his gift.

acey: You not gonna wait until this evening?

ire: Maybe it'll give me an idea.

Wire takes the lid off the box.
Pulls out an African Talking Drum.

Vire: This don't help me none. What is this?

tacey: A talking drum.

Vire: Talking drum …?

tacey: From Africa.

Vire: Why'd she give me this? I cain't play music.

tacey: =.=

Vire: Nobody sells anything from Africa around here.

   Where'd those two women find this?

Stacey: Who knows.

Wire taps at the drum with his fingers.

Stacey: There's something else in there.

Wire takes out a pamphlet from the box.

Wire: Instructions.

Reading the pamphlet, Wire learns how *
hold the drum. He tucks it under his arm.
takes the beater and lightly taps the head.
Stacey watches him. As the beating persist
Stacey sits forward.
As Wire's drumming grows in force a you
Factory Folk runs into the shop. Winded.

Factory Folk: Truth! Truth! We need bandages, rags, towels, and a whole
bucket of ice.

Stacey and Wire rush out of the bedroom,
enter the shop.

Truth: What's goin on?

Factory Folk: No … first-aid in the … factory. One of the Evans boys …
passed out at the grinder machine. Got his hand caught in
We gotta wrap him up and take him to the hospital. Lost a
lot of blood. Had to use the head of a mop to wrap his han
in …

Truth and Stacey snatch up a bunch of
supplies. Green smoke bellows from the
factory pipes.

Stacey: Keep an eye on the store, Wire.

Wire stands holding his drum.

Truth, Stacey, and Factory Folk exit out the
front door in a rush, carrying rags and
supplies.

Wire is alone in the shop.

He taps on the drum. He hears something.

Taps again. Listens.

He taps, this time changing the pitch of the
tone.

He continues to tap and listen as the lights fade to black.

TWO.

Evening of the same day.

In the distance, thin green smoke seeps from the factory pipes into the bruised sky.

Sunny is on the front porch, decorating it for the party. She wears the same dress she wore in the previous act. She hangs up Christmas lights.

Patricia sits in the shop, rolling cigarettes. She wears a very fancy black satin dress. A handkerchief is tucked between her breasts.

Patricia: This is some good shit I got. I can smell how good it is.

Sunny: What do you call it again?

Patricia: Grinds. It's Stacey's favorite even though he don't smoke it too often. Last time I saw him smoke was at this house party. He was flyin. He never danced like that with me since. I've seen him dance with other ...folks [*meaning men*] like that, but it was the first and the last with me.

Sunny: Y'all dance all the time in your act, don't you?

Patricia: Yea, but we're dancing for laughs, for applause. That night at that party ... you ever dance real nice with somebody Sunny?

Sunny: Not like the way you talkin.

Patricia: Koko Taylor was jamming with this band. And Stacey had a hold of me ... he pulled up my skirt a lil bit and snaked his leg in between mine ... he had unbuttoned his shirt had on a tank-top underneath and I had on this deep scoop neck cotton number and I could feel the hairs on his chest pressin into my chest ...

Sunny: Oooo, I didn't know y'all got down like that.

Patricia: We don't. We didn't. He was high. I was too.

He held on to me until the sun came up and then he let go. We did a show the next night and it was back to:

> *Patricia sings a verse from "How High t Moon." As she sings, Sunny attention is drawn to a scene in the distance. She stan trying to make it out.*

> *As it comes closer Sunny is shocked and disgusted. She covers her mouth.*

Patricia: Oh, Sunny, I need me a good time something awful. Things ain't been as good as they used to be. Stayin on top is hard when you keep gettin knocked down. At least when you got somebody wit you, both of you can keep each other upright. I don't like bein by myself …. Cain't tolerate it.

=.=

I'm glad we found each other, Sunny.

> *Stacey and Truth climb the steps, blood splattered on them like a paint job gone baa On the porch, they remove their shoes and socks. Exhausted and devastated, they walk past a speechless Sunny and enter the shop. Patricia looks up, stands up. Truth walks pa her into Stacey's room out the back door onto the porch where he removes all his clothes. H leaves them in a heap on the back porch. He stands in his underwear and washes himself from the basin on.*

Stacey: Where's Wire?

Patricia: What happened to y'all?

Stacey: Did he leave the shop empty?

Patricia: No, he was here when we showed up to decorate. He got word that woman had a girl. Had to go tell the … Stacey what did y'all get into?

Stacey [*a bit dazed*]: Somebody got hurt at the factory. We had to help get him to the hospital.

Patricia: Did you know him?

Stacey: He was a part of the Evans family. Ivory Evans great-great grandson. Emekah Evans.

Sunny enters the shop. Still speechless.

cey: =.=

=.= [*unbuttons his shirt*]

He's gone.

=.=

=.= [*removes his shirt. he wears a tank top underneath*]

The hospital's a ways away from here.

=.=

=.=

We was half way there when he stopped screaming. We just turned the truck back around and took him to the funeral home.

> *Truth finishes washing himself, changes the water.*
>
> *Stacey crosses to his bedroom. Takes off his pants and tank-top. Stands in his underwear. Looks at his hands covered in blood.*
>
> *Truth enters Stacey's room.*

ruth: Did I get it all off me?

tacey [*looks*]: Yea.

ruth: You got some clothes I could borrow.

tacey: Under the bed. Took em off the line this morning.

> *Stacey goes to the back porch to clean himself.*
>
> *Truth picks from Stacey's clothes. Puts on a shirt and pants. Walks out into the shop barefoot. He crosses to his backpack and pulls out a bottle of whiskey. He takes a swig.*

Truth: We was in the bed of the truck with him. Took all six of us to load him in the back. All 6'3", one-hundred-and-ninety-five-pounds of him. On our way to the hospital … blood was—

Sunny [*a bit hysterical*]: I don't wanna hear it. Can't take stories like this, Patricia. I'm sorry. Cain't listen to whatever he got to say.

Patricia: Gone outside on the porch. Here. [*gives Sunny a smoke*] Get this started I'll be out there in a minute.

41

Sunny takes the grind. Steps out on the
porch. Paces and smokes.

Patricia [*to Truth*]: Not too loud. She don't need to know about it anyway.
Truth: =.= [*drinks*]
Emekah was knocked out cold for most of the ride,
and then his eyes pop open and he starts screaming for his cap.
Ivory's picture is ... sewn in his cap. "My Ivory's gone! Where's my
muthafuckin cap! Where's my goddamn cap! Ivory!" We find it ove
Truth (*cont'd*):
in the corner. I reach for it and show it to him. And, and he takes it
with his one hand and puts it over his face.
Ivory's picture is on his face. And he screams.
"You was right. Like weeds. You was right. Oh, Lord. Messiah."
And he was screaming "Ivory messiah, Ivory messiah" until he ...
stopped.

Patricia exhales at the end of the story.
Stacey enters into his bedroom and puts on
fresh pair of clothes.

Truth: They whole city's gonna be still for a few days.
Until the Evans announce the arrangements.
=.=
=.=
Sunny can take them lights down while she out there.
No party tonight.
Patricia: What you gonna do, Truth?
Truth: I'ma sit here for a minute. My legs still loose. Don't know if I'll be
able to walk home.
=.=
=.=
What'd you give her?
Patricia: Grinds.
Truth: Where'd you get that?
Patricia: Asked around. You wanna spark?
Truth: =.= [*thinks about it*]
It ain't good to get messed up the night somebody you know dies.

Truth puts the cap back on the bottle and
puts it in his backpack.
Stacey enters the shop. Sits.

Patricia [*pandering*]: Stacey, honey, I got you a present …

Stacey [*cynical*]: A present? And it ain't even my birthday?

> *Patricia dismisses his tone, shows him the smoke.*

Patricia: Truth got some issues with relaxing tonight. But …
I know it ain't right to have a party, but we shouldn't spend the whole night propped up like chumps.

Stacey: You want some other clothes to put on?

Patricia: =.=
=.=
What's wrong with my dress …?

Stacey: =.=

Patricia: What's wrong with it?

Stacey: I don't wanna look at you in that dress.

Patricia: Why not?

Stacey: That's a dress you wear performing. I don't wanna think about performing. And that's what I'ma think about with you skipping around in that damn dress.

Truth: You wear that onstage?

Patricia: Yes I do.

Truth: That's a nice piece. Very nice.

Stacey: Don't encourage her, Truth …

Truth: It is.

Patricia: And Stacey had a white three piece with a black trim … you know what I'm talkin about, Stacey.

Stacey: No, no, no! Patricia, I don't wanna hash.

Patricia: I ain't hashing with you. I'm describing how it was to Truth.
[*to Truth*] And Stacey and I would do this coming-home-from-a-house-party bit …

> *Frustrated, Stacey goes out onto the front porch with Sunny.*
> *Patricia continues with Truth.*

Patricia: He and I are playing like we bout to have a one-night stand, you know? And we do this whole exchange about how I like to get down and how he likes to get down. He's talkin all big about what kinda lover he is, "I'ma tear that pussy up…" all that talk. But the joke starts when the way I like to get down gets freakier and

43

Patricia *(cont'd):*

>freakier until he starts gettin scared shitless ... I'm sayin, "I'm b
>to give you some Kunta Kinte strokes, muthafucka ..." and he's
>tremblin, too drunk to run straight for the door. I got him corne
>and then I tell him, "now take off your clothes and get on your j
>b."

>>*Truth cracks up laughing. Patricia laugh
>>too.*

>>*On the front porch ... Stacey sits with
>>Sunny.*

Sunny [*already a little blazed*]: This shit is pretty good.
Stacey: You sure you need any more.
Sunny: You right. You probably right.

>>*Sunny takes one more big hit, then gives*
>>*to Stacey who puts it out.*

Sunny [*thinking he took a hit*]: Isn't that good?
Stacey [*smiles*]: Mm-hm.
Sunny: =.=
Stacey: =.=

>=.=
>=.= [*Truth laughs at a joke Patricia tells*]
>I'm sorry the party is a bust.

Sunny: Ain't a bust to me. I been to some shitty parties. This ain't one of
em. It ain't the best one I been to but it ain't the worst.
Stacey: What's the best one you been to?
Sunny: My 6th grade graduation party.
Stacey: That was the best one? Really?
Sunny: Mm-hm.
Stacey: What made it good?
Sunny: I got a new dress. Got a brand new Strawberry Shortcake
notebook. And one of them graduation caps. Mine was pink.
What's the best party you been to?
Stacey: =.= [*thinking about it*]
My 16th birthday party.
Sunny: What was so good about it?

>>*Stacey smiles. He can't help himself. The*
>>*memory of it is too good.*

Sunny: Ooooo, you musta got some!

Stacey laughs. It's true.

Sunny: Ooooo. From Patricia?
Stacey: No! No. Uh-uh. Somebody else … it was kind of like a present.
Sunny: I bet no gift was the same after that!

Sunny laughs. Stacey laughs.

In the shop, Patricia hears this and looks in their direction.

Ruth: What's wrong?
Patricia: Just makin sure they alright.

On the front porch:

Sunny: =.=
         =.=
         You wanna know the worst one I been to?
Stacey: Yea.
Sunny: It's more recent.
Stacey: How recent?
Sunny: Five days ago.
         =.=
         =.=
         I was supposed to marry this man.
         =.=
         But I ran away.

Sunny cracks up laughing.

Stacey: For real?
Sunny: Uh-huh. It was an engagement party. Horrible.
Stacey: Who is he?
Sunny: My father and his father got drunk 20 years ago and promised each other their kids would marry. I'm the girl. He's the boy. We had to jump. I couldn't say no.
Stacey: Why not?
Sunny: That's how things go down. Drunk promises are like blood oaths. Especially between the men folk. I was gonna have to marry this bearish dude and have his kids cause my daddy wants to play house.

45

Stacey: So you ran away.

Sunny: I ran away. No clothes. No unmentionables. Only this [*re: her dress*]. I'm sorry I couldn't get all dressed up like Patricia …

Stacey: You don't have to worry about that, Sunny. I think your dress is pretty. Does Patricia know about your … situation?

Sunny: I told her somewhere around hour seven on the bus. But I think she was asleep …

Stacey: How'd you runaway?

Sunny: Said I needed to pray by myself.

So I prayed on the way to the bus station. Prayed at the ticket counter. Prayed on the bus and when I opened my eyes Patricia wa asking if anybody was sitting next to me …

Stacey: You cain't go back?

Sunny: If I go back, I'm a wife, a mother. It's over.

Stacey: What is?

Sunny: Sunny. I am. Me. I'm over. I'd be Mrs. Leon Moore. Mrs. Leon Whack. Mrs. Whack.

Stacey: What if they come lookin for you?

Sunny: Everybody's poor. They can only afford to carry the shame. Leon'll be alright. Men always have a plan B. Women ain't allowed such security.

Stacey: You made your own plan B.

Sunny [*discovers a pride in this*]: That's right. I did.

=.=

=.=

Patricia is so cool.

Stacey: =.=

Sunny: I know y'all having issues … but you cain't deny how glamorous she is. I been watching her live [*as in 'alive'*] for [*counts it out*] almos 20 hours now and it's the best show ever.

=.=

=.=

That must've been nice dancing with her.

Stacey: On stage?

Sunny: Naw, at the Ko Ko Taylor party. That must've been nice. Do you remember that? I would've remembered that …

Stacey: What'd she tell you?

Sunny: Chests pressed up against each other. Legs getting wrapped up. Wang dang DAMN … It's hot. Are you hot?

Stacey: Uh-uh.

ny: I had to dance with the man I was supposed to marry, and it
wasn't nuthin like the way Patricia was describing it.
=.=
=.=
You think she'd dance real nice with me?

cey: =.= [*speechless*]

ny: Huh Stacey? You seen her dance with other folks?
=.=
=.=
Stacey … ?

In the shop:

tricia [*to Truth*]: Is it too blasphemous in your handbook to play a bit
of music tonight?

uth: Not unless you want that Evans boy showing up at the party.

tricia: Aw, now, don't talk no mumbo about souls flying …

uth: I don't have to. You already know.

tricia [*playful pout*]: Truth, it's my birthday. You don't want us to have a
good time?

uth: Uh-uh. It's Wire's birthday. And he ain't here no way.

atricia: It's about to be my birthday. If you don't wanna have a good
time with me at least give me a gift.

uth: From where?

atricia [*Duh*]: We standin in a store, brotha man. You can put it on my tab.
=.= [*smiles*]
I'ma close my eyes …

uth: Like hide and seek?

atricia: Kinda … except you put my gift on the counter and then I open
my eyes to see it.

Truth laughs. Stacey notices this.

Truth: Alright.

Truth looks around the store.

Patricia: Should I close my eyes?

Truth: Not yet. I'm still deciding.
=.= [*looking*]
=.= [*looking*]

While Truth is deciding, Patricia glances at the front porch. Stacey and Sunny still talking.

Truth: Okay! I know what it is. Close your eyes.

Patricia closes her eyes. Truth crosses over and digs out an object from a box. He holds it behind his back, faces Patricia.

Truth: Open.

Patricia opens her eyes. Looks around.

Patricia: Where is it?
Truth: Behind me.
Patricia: Show it to me.
Truth: You gotta promise me something first.
Patricia: Truth, that's a tacky thing. A birthday gift with strings attached.
Truth: It's a thin string. Only one. Lotta slack, too. So … you don't have to
    promise to make it happen. Just try to arrange circumstances my wa
Patricia [*a bit wary*]: What?
Truth [*intimate*]: I'm ready to settle down, Patricia.
Patricia [*wariness grows*]: Okay …
Truth: I been around too many bodies on the brink of death or insanity.
    First the invasion, then Mister Good senior,
    And sittin in the back of that truck watching that Evans' boy flail wa
    the final alarm … I don't wanna be alone anymore.
Patricia: What you expect me to do about that?
Truth [*so as not to be heard from the front porch*]: Get me Sunny.
Patricia: Sunny?
Truth: Uh-huh.
Patricia: Truth, she ain't lookin for a—

Truth reveals Patricia's birthday gift: a bar of soap in the shape of an airplane. A toy a child would play with at bath time.

Patricia is taken aback.

Truth: It's soap. Smells like roses.
Patricia: Oh …

ath: It's funny, see, cause you travel a lot. Cause you'll be in some far
   away land taking a bath with an airplane.

ricia: Thank you ... Truth.

ath: Take it.

> *Patricia takes the gift. A polite smile.*

> *On the back porch a drunk Wire climbs the
> steps. His talking drum is slug over his
> shoulder. He sits on the step. Giggles. Quiets
> himself.*

tricia: I'll put it right ... [*looks around*] here [*places it in a drawer behind
   the counter*] for safe keepin, okay, uh-huh.

> *Truth smiles.*

uth: Does that mean you'll help me?

tricia: I will. I will help you, Truth. But I got a deal to make with you.

uth [*now he's a bit wary*]: Okay ...

tricia: I got offers to play nice houses overseas, but they want me <u>and</u>
   Stacey for half the performance then I'd do my solo material for
   the other half.

ruth: You want me to help you get Stacey back?

atricia: Not exactly ... I want you to help me get Wire to travel with me.

ruth: Wire? I thought you'd want ...

atricia: I do. I do. But he came back only cause of Wire. Stacey don't
   care about this shop two ways for nuthin.

ruth: He don't?

atricia: No.

Truth: But, but if I get Wire to leave with you and Stacey follows, the
   documents say the store closes. I'ma have to go work in the factory.
   I'ma be a Factory Folk.

atricia: Do you want Sunny or not?

Truth: She ain't gonna want me if I'm covered in pencil shavings.

Patricia: We'll change the documents then. Give the store to you. I'll pay
   somebody to find a loop hole.

Truth: Mister Good senior clogged up every crack and hole. When he
   started getting paranoid, he had Hunter Priestess put a hex on it.
   Nobody in the city will touch it. Afraid of the bad that comes with
   it—

> *Sunny climbs to her feet. Walks into the shop.*

Sunny [*announcement*]: I have to visit the restroom out back.
Patricia: How you feeling, Sunny?
Sunny: =.= [*cotton mouth*]
　　　　　I'ma need some water.
　　　　　But first I have to visit the restroom out back.
Patricia: Do you need me to come with you?

> *Sunny smiles. Gap. Truth's heart melts.*
> *Sunny giggles. Smiles.*

Sunny: No, Patricia. I'm, I'll be alright.

> *Sunny crosses the shop, she sheepishly waves*
> *at Truth, exits. Truth is smitten.*

Truth [*to Patricia*]: You got a deal.

> *Sunny crosses through Stacey's bedroom.*
> *Enters the back door. She jumps back when*
> *she see Wire sitting on the steps.*
>
> *Wire looks up. Grins. Smiles.*

Wire: Hey hey, Sunny! Oooo, I like my birthday gift. Thank you.
Sunny: Oh! oh, oh … it's just you. I'm glad you like your gift. That makes
　　　　me happy, Patrick—
Wire: Wire.
Sunny: Uh-huh, but I have to visit the …
　　　　　=.= [*cotton mouth*]
　　　　　My mouth is so dry.
Wire: There's a water pitcher over there.

> *Wire waves his beater in the general*
> *direction of the basin and water pitcher.*
> *Sunny crosses over to it. Hovers over the*
> *pitcher. Goes in to pick it up, but of course*
> *she picks up the basin that Stacey washed*
> *himself in. She drinks the water with the*
> *Evans' boy blood in it. Wire taps on his*
> *drum.*

Sunny drinks then puts the basin down.

Sunny: I think there was a bug in that …

=.=

Restroom. Now.

Sunny exits.

Wire climbs to his feet.

Wire [*yells from the back porch*]: Hey hey now!

Stacey [*from the front porch*]: Hey hey. Birthday boy!

Wire enters the bedroom. Stacey enters the shop. Wire enters the shop all drunk and smiling …

Patricia: Look like he's getting back from a party.

Wire: Is it over?

Stacey: It never got started.

Truth: That Evans' boy passed away.

Stacey: Emekah.

Wire: Oh.

=.=

=.=

That's sad to hear that.

=.=

=.=

Hurt himself that bad, huh?

Stacey: Yea.

Wire: Bad luck to be drunk the day a man dies. But I didn't know.
When I left to tell that daddy about his daughter I didn't know
nuthin about it.

Patricia: Is that where you got all sauced?

Wire: Yes, ma'am.

=.=

But I didn't know about Emekah.
Or else I woulda passed when they sent the bottle around.
Would <u>not</u> have told them it was my birthday.
Would <u>not</u> have played them "Wang Dang Doodle" … [*sings*] *all
night long …*
[*spoken*] They liked my drum, too.

51

Wire *(cont'd):*

    [*to Patricia*] Thank you so much for this drum, Patricia. I'ma trust this gesture is comin from a good place 'cause I like it so much. I know you live and breathe off ulterior motives, but I'ma hope you a diet from it—

Truth: Wire, maybe you oughta go rest on Stacey's bed.

Wire: Now, wait a minute now, just cause we lost somebody today don't mean we cain't try to have a good time.

Truth: I think that is what it means. It means exactly that.

Wire: Truth, Truth you are being unnecessarily stupid.

Stacey: Okay … Wire—

Wire: I busted my ass getting back here to spend my birthday with y'all. Them minin folk were real nice to me. First time in … I don't know when … that I played my song and other people danced with me. I left all that to come here.

Patricia: Uh-uh. Clearly you left there to come back here and get pissy with us.

Wire: I came back here cause it's our party. You said you was throwin a party.

Truth: And we said a man died tonight.

Wire: I'm 30 years old. Patty, you gonna be 30 years old, too.

Patricia: I know …

Wire: Mama had us when she was 30. What I'ma have? What you gonna have, Patty, huh?

Patricia: The way you carryin on I'ma have a headache—

Wire: That new daddy I was drinkin with tonight, he's 22.

    Twenty-damn-two! Got a wife and a child, working the mines—a good, steady job. On my way back here, I was scratchin my head tryna remember: where was my thinkin when I was 22? I wasn't wrapped up in no family that's for sure. I was wrapped up in waitin. Bidin my time. Just waitin for … [*looks at Stacey*]. Writin letters. Just waitin … yearnin through my birthdays, through the invasion …. Waitin through everything.

    And, and tonight I was standin in front of this brotha who was tearin up over the birth of his daughter. And, and then he was nice enough to celebrate his daughter <u>and me</u>. He didn't even know who I was beyond payin me to bring him a message but he celebrated me.

    Y'all know what that's like? Not for writing a funny joke, or singing a pretty song or stocking a crappy shelf but for being alive. Celebrated for being born.

    =.=

=.=
I hate I still wanna give that to you, Patty. I do.
But it's your birthday—our birthday
I still want both of us to feel celebrated. Like we used to.
=.=
=.= [getting a little sick]
 I, I, I'ma need some air …

> *Wire stumbles across the room, heading for the front porch. Stacey goes to him, but Patricia holds him back.*
> *She crosses over to Wire and helps him out onto the porch. She helps him sit.*
>
> *Truth and Stacey are left in the shop.*
>
> *A puff of green smoke shines in the night sky above the factory.*

Stacey: =.=

Truth: =.=

Stacey: =.=

Truth: Your daddy was the same way as that young cat Wire was talkin bout. He was the same way when I told him about you.

Stacey: He didn't know about me?

Truth: No, he did. He just didn't know if you were a boy or a girl.
He was stuck in another county negotiating the price for a order of … [*tries to remember*] hair grease. That's when everybody, men and women, were wearing their hair long and up with a fist full of grease. Your daddy couldn't keep it on the shelves.
He was arguing with a distributor, trying to get the price down when I ran in and told him he had a son.
He was so happy. I remember seeing tears. He was young, too. Younger than that cat Wire was talking about.

Stacey: Were you?

Truth: What?

Stacey: Happy.

Truth: Hell no. Are you for real? Uh-uh.

Stacey: Why?

Truth: I was a boy. Around 7 or 8. Your daddy was the only daddy I knew.

Stacey: I took your limelight …

Truth: Yea … among other things.

On the front porch Wire sits, holding onto his drum. Patricia stands, leaning against post. She smokes.

Wire: =.=
    =.= [*tap, tap*]
This is the worst party I ever been to.
Patricia: That's a fine way to deal with things.
Wire: You cain't say all this is fun, Patty.
Patricia: Nobody said it was, but at least I'm polite enough to keep my
    mouth shut.
Wire: For what? Who I'm gonna offend with the truth?
Patricia: Me. Sunny. Stacey—
Wire: Shit, the way Stacey been treatin me … he's the one flickin offenses
    all over the damn place.
Patricia: =.=
    =.=
    =.=
How he been treatin you?

Wire gives Patricia the side eye.

Patricia: What?
Wire: I ain't that messed up. You think I'ma tell you all that?
Patricia: You don't think I can help? I been on the road with him for the
    past 10 years … I know every crease in his thinkin and every note
    in his voice.
Wire: That don't make you an expert on his heart though.
Patricia: =.=
    =.= [*this is true*]
    =.= [*smokes*]
You right.
    =.=
Damn. Mhm.
Wire: =.=
    =.= [*tap, tap on the drum*]
You got issues with me.
Patricia: That's the liquor talkin.
Wire: That's the truth talkin. Liquor or not. We twins. I can feel you; you
    can feel me.
    =.=
    =.= [*tap, tap*]
I got issues with you too.

Patricia: =.=

=.= [*smokes*]

This is a party, Wire.

We got lots of other occasions to scratch at each other. Don't have to get into it now.

Wire: Who's gettin into anything?

Patricia: You tryin to.

Wire: Uh-uh. I'm just tryin to have a good birthday … ain't you tryin to have a good birthday, Patty?

In the shop with Stacey and Truth.

Stacey: =.=

Truth: =.=

Stacey: =.=

Truth: You did well today. Handlin that Evans' ride.

Stacey: =.=

=.=

Thank you.

=.=

=.=

You did, too.

=.=

=.=

We need a hospital closer to here.

Truth: It's cheaper to bury us than to save us.

Stacey: =.=

Truth: =.=

Stacey: Maybe I'll get into politics. Try to better some things.

Truth: Around here?

Stacey: Yea.

Truth: You ain't heard none of the stories about the invasion?

Stacey: =.=

=.=

Yea … I kept up with things while I was on the road.

Truth: Hearin bits of something before you go on stage to tell jokes about shootin craps ain't really "keeping up."

Stacey: Wire was writin to me. Like he said. He was tellin me what was goin down—

Truth: Then you ought to know gettin into politics is crawlin into a early grave.

Stacey: =.=

Truth: Closed casket, too.

Stacey: =.=
Truth: =.=
Stacey: =.=

Stacey lights up a smoke. Takes a hit.

Truth: Smokin that shit don't help either.
Stacey: You ain't that much older than me, Truth. Why you crickin
    around like you Frederick Douglass or something?
Truth: Better than bein ignorant all the damn time—
Stacey: I know what happened here, okay? I know they capped folks, took
    lives without blinkin twice. I know. And that factory ain't nuthin b
    a reminder of the takeover. But shit, can I at least try to change sor
    things? I know what I'm doin. Know what I wanna fix out there ar
Stacey *(cont'd)*:
    how to take care of things in here. I know how to fill out a
    damn inventory sheet, know how to count the till. And I know how
    to smoke some grinds and not get twisted.
Truth: =.=
Stacey: =.=
Truth: =.=
Stacey: =.=
Truth: Do you know why your daddy really had to jet outta town?
Stacey: =.=
Truth: =.=

    =.=
    Huh?
Stacey: =.= [*He doesn't*]
Truth: He got chased out.

    =.=
    =.=
    And not by no debt or no affair ...
    Not by what you can see, but what you feel.
    =.=
    =.=
    =.=
    Said the devil was after him.
    Said he'd be in bed in that back room just like you do now
    and he'd open his eyes to the devil standin over him, pissin fire on his
    sheets.
    =.=
    =.=
    He stopped sleepin.

=.=
Made me sit up with him thru night with a rifle in my lap and a .45 in his.
Me. I did that for your daddy.
=.=
=.=
You a waste, Stacey. Ain't worth the pot you shit in …

Stacey: =.=
Truth: =.=
Stacey: =.=
Truth: Disappointment.
Stacey: =.=
=.=
Truth: You think you funny?
You ain't. Patty makes me laugh. But you, you make me cry. Make a grown man cry—
Stacey: Instead of talkin bullshit to me why don't you go find my daddy? That's what you want, ain't it? To crawl up under my father so you can keep playin house for the rest of your life? Why you hangin around here? I don't need a 35 year-old son—
Truth: Cause all this was supposed to be mine!
=.=
=.=
All of this was promised to me and I cain't leave it. I won't leave it. You were supposed to be a girl! You were promised to me! I was supposed to be your husband! You was supposed to come out a girl and I was gonna marry you and your daddy was gonna give me this damn shop!
=.=
When I was 6 years old he promised me … promised me … right at that counter. Said I was gonna marry his daughter. Be his son. He said I could add on a house in the back to raise a family in …
=.=
I was cryin the whole way when I ran to tell your daddy how you came out. I thought he was gonna be upset. I thought he was gonna be disappointed that he couldn't have me … but, but he was happy. That muthafucka was overjoyed!
=.=
And just like that … I ain't got nothin. Or nobody. All I do is watch this fuckin shop day in, day out. Sweep the damn floors, clean the windows. But none of it is mine. Never will be …. I felt like I ain't had no plan B for most of my life. 'Til today. Til that gal walked thru that door with that smile …

57

*Just then Sunny climbs up the steps onto th[e]
back porch. Her gait altered. Wide stance.
Her left hand curled up in a knot. She blo[ws]
green smoke from her mouth. She sings wi[th]
a new voice, a different voice, a man's voic[e]
... a sweet tenor reminiscent of Donny
Hathaway or Sam Cooke ... she sings wit[h]
the voice of a dislocated soul: Emekah Eva[ns]
...*

Sunny: *Ivory, my Ivory, coastin 'long the sea.*
Ivory, my Ivory, wonderin who she'll be.
The sun behind her.
The grass below.
She walked until she walked no more ....

*Stacey, Truth, Wire then Patricia face the
direction of the voice.*

Wire and Patricia enter the shop.

*Sunny steps into Stacey's bedroom. She knock[s]
aside anything near her path.*

*She pulls back the curtain stands in the
doorway of the shop.*

*Sunny looks at the room. The room looks at
her.*

Sunny: *A mama calls ...*
A daddy calls ...
A brother calls ...
A sister calls ...
And the devil answered in Ivory tears.
Brown Ivory's red, red tears.

*Sunny enters the shop, holds up her knotted
hand, offering it to the heavens.*

Sunny: *Ivory stopped and fell to her knees.*
She saw her people pulled a part like weeds.
[hushed] I saw it, too.
The heavens behind her.
The hells below.

She screamed until she screamed no more.

=.=

Ivory messiah. Ivory messiah. Messiah ….

=.=

=.=

[*spoken:*] Hey hey now.

HREE.

> *Night that same day. In the shop Sunny /*
> *Emekah (rhymes with eureka) Evans is*
> *bound to a chair that's bound to the counter.*
> *Everyone in the room breathes heavy. A*
> *wrestling match has just ended. The front of*
> *Patricia's dress is ripped. Wire's drum is*
> *broken. Clothes are ruffled and ripped. A*
> *green haze surrounds Sunny's body.*

Truth: =.= [*catching his breath*]

Stacey: =.= [*catching his breath*]

Patricia: =.= [*breathing, holding her dress up against her body*]

Emekah Sunny**:** =.= [*breathing*]

Wire: =.= [*breathing*]

Emekah Sunny**:** Y'all got to tie a muthafucka up like an animal?

Stacey: You act like one, get treated like one.

Wire: Coulda been worse.

Emekah Sunny**:** Fuck you, coulda been worse. Shiiiiiiiiiiiit …

Truth: =.=

Emekah Sunny**:** =.=

Stacey: =.=

Patricia: =.=

Wire: =.=

Emekah Sunny**:** Comin at me like that. Who the fuck y'all think y'all are?

Wire: =.= [*breathing*]

Patricia: =.= [*looking at Emekah / Sunny. Turns away.*]

Emekah Sunny**:** These ropes are too tight! Y'all den made this shit too …

> *Wire, Truth and Stacey look at Emekah /*
> *Sunny squirm. It's clear that the knots are*

too strong for Emekah / Sunny to break. The
room relaxes a bit in this realization.

Truth grabs the bottle of whiskey from his
backpack. He takes a swig then passes it to
Patricia who takes a swig then passes it to
Wire who drinks then passes it to Stacey.
Stacey drinks then returns it to Truth.

Truth is devastated by the turn of events.

Patricia [*to Stacey; hushed*]: I'ma need a change of clothes …
Stacey: In my room. Under the bed.

Patricia exits the shop. Enters Stacey's room.
She finds a pair of pants and shirt. Changes
her clothes as:

Emekah Sunny: This gurl got some nice skin why y'all wanna ruin it makin
        these ropes so tight?
Stacey: Cause you punched me, scratched Truth, broke Wire's drum,
       busted up Patricia's dress …
Truth: And now you squattin in that poor girl's body …
Wire: You den created a whole heap of mess in a short bit of time,
      Emekah Evans.
Emekah Sunny: You can kiss my black ass, Wire. All y'all can.
        Shit, why y'all ain't askin why I got hurt at that machine?!
        Why y'all ain't hollerin at the owner about getting some
        damn first aide in that factory??
        Or, or getting a hospital 'round here? Worried about some
        damn gal … what about <u>me</u>?!
        Is she even from around here?
        [*checks out the body*]
        Got some nice credentials though …
        Cain't wait to get loose up in here—

Patricia exits the bedroom, enters the shop
wearing Stacey's clothes.

Emekah Sunny: Oooo wee! Patty sweets Patty. I didn't know you was in
       town … Stacey come back and you come sniffin after him,
       huh baby girl?

Patricia crosses over to the bottle of whiskey.
As she drinks she flips Emekah /Sunny the
bird.

Emekah Sunny: Awww, come on now, Patty baby. You cain't take a joke?
That's your job, ain't it? Takin jokes. Long, thick, throbbin
jokes? I'm just playin. I'm just messin with you. Don't be
mad. I'll make it up to you. Come over here and have a seat
on this lap. I'll make you feel all better—

Patricia: Rather sit down on a bear trap.

Emekah Sunny: Damn! Cold-blooded. No wonder you had to cut her ass
loose, Stacey—

Stacey: What the hell do you want, Emekah?

Emekah Sunny: I don't want or need your uppity attitudes that's for damn
sure. Got enough of that bullshit from the folks at the
factory.
Damn, a brotha dies and still dealin with shittalkers—

Truth: Cause that brotha is bustin in places he ain't got no business in.

Emekah Sunny: I got plenty of business. Lots of stuff I need to 'tend to.
You thinkin I knew today was gonna be my last?
I ain't planned for none of this to happen.
Treatin me like a thug.

Truth: You cain't stay in there, Emekah.

Emekah Sunny: This gal pulled at me … y'all think I'm the kind of man
who just pushes his way into some female? I only enter if
I'm invited and this invitation landed on me at exactly the
right time.
When my body died in the back of that truck, I was sucked
out through the belly button and shot out like a bullet from
a gun. I was zipping and screaming through the universe.
Knowing whatever I was gonna hit was gonna get hit <u>hard</u>.
Shit, I was going too fast for the landing <u>not</u> to be a mess.
You heard me? And then I fell plop down into this pretty
young thing.

Patricia drinks more whiskey. Seeing this
gesture, Wire remembers. He jumps up and
runs to the back porch to see the empty basin.

Wire [*yells from the back porch*]: The basin is empty. She was thirsty. She was
so messed up she musta drank from the basin.

Stacey [*to Patricia and Truth*]: And I didn't change the water from the
accident …

Patricia: All that blood …

They all get grossed out.
Wire enters Stacey's room, reenters the sh[...]

Patricia: We got to get this fool outta her …
Emekah Sunny**:** Uh-uh. Cain't do that, Sadity Bop.
I gotta get to my family.
Got to get to my people's house to figure out what I shoul[...]
do.
And I need this body to get me there.
Stacey: Why you got to get back to your family?
Truth: What does it matter?! He cain't stay!
Emekah Sunny**:** Cause I wasn't supposed to go flyin. Wasn't supposed to zip
and scream. Ivory was supposed to be there.
She was supposed to meet me when I left my body but
instead I just went flying. That ain't how it's supposed to
happen. My ancestor is supposed to take me in her arms.
Supposed to bless me. Walk me to my paradise.
Stacey: So you sittin up in Sunny cause Ivory was runnin late?
Emekah Sunny**:** You got jokes! Fuck you, Ms. Stacey.
Stacey: What'd you say to me?
Emekah Sunny**:** Get me to my family.
Stacey: I'ma get you uh ass kickin if you—
Patricia: Don't put a hand on her, Stacey, don't!

Stacey steps back.

Truth: You ain't takin her nowhere, Emekah. Especially not to that Evans'
property. Ain't no tellin what your people gonna do to her tryin to
get you to Ivory.
Emekah Sunny**:** I'm not leavin this body.
Truth: I heard your dumb ass, but you gettin out anyway.

Truth grabs a plastic sandwich bag from a
box that rests on a shelf.

Truth: Wire come on out here …

Truth crosses into Stacey's room Wire
follows. Truth grabs a pencil and paper. Goes
out onto the back porch.

He removes his handkerchief, swabs the inside of the bowl, folds it and puts it in the sandwich bag, gives it to Wire. Then he writes on the piece of paper.

In the shop Patricia, Stacey, Emekah / Sunny.

mekah Sunny: Patricia and Stacey, keepin it real!
[*chuckles*]
There was some funny shit on that album.
<u>Most</u> of it was alright, but some of it was funny.

Patricia: You talkin all this mess cause you know these men don't hit women. Crawl up in Truth and see if Stacey don't smack you around then.

Emekah Sunny: I heard they was talkin bout givin y'all the key to the city.

Patricia [*instantly diverted*]: Really?

Stacey [*not now …*]: Patricia …

Patricia [*to Stacey*]: Did you know about this?

Stacey: Yes.

Patricia: And you wasn't gonna tell me?

Emekah Sunny [*to Patricia*]: Wasn't gonna say a damn thing, gurl—

Stacey: Shut up, Emekah. [*to Patricia*] Ain't no point in talkin about it.

Patricia: You didn't turn it down, did you?

Stacey: Of course I turned it down.

Emekah Sunny: Mhm. Woulda been a nice ceremony, too.
Glazed ham … wine coolers … brass band …

Patricia: You up and said no without hearin word from me?

Stacey: The last set of words you gave me was a "fuck" and a "you."
And that's after you slapped me.
You expect I'ma write you about some damn key to the city?

Patricia: That's how we do, Stacey.
We yell and bitch at each other and then one of us walks away.
But we always make up when we step on stage.
It's how we do.

Stacey: Uh-uh. Ain't how we do. Not no more.

Emekah Sunny: Oooooo—

Patricia & Stacey: Shut up!

On the back porch Truth finishes up his note. Folds it up. Gives it to Wire.

Truth: Take this note and that sample to Waymon Davis. Over yonder. Tell him to get here as fast as he can make it.

Wire: Y'all gonna be alright?

Truth: We'll be fine. Gone to him.

> *Wire zips through Stacey's room, into the shop, grabs his broken drum, runs out the front door, jumps off the front porch.*
>
> *He's gone.*
>
> *Truth trails behind at a much slower pace. He enters the shop as:*

Emekah Sunny: That sonofabitch Wire is quick! Runnin out like a jug of liquor. Speakin of which … [*smacks his/her lips*] y'all was passin that around and forgot me.

Patricia: We didn't forget.

Emekah Sunny: Well I'm askin.

Stacey: No, Emekah.

Emekah Sunny: Do y'all Sadity Bops realize what I been through today? I don't think y'all really know …

Truth: Uh, I think we do. I was holdin your head up when you took your last breath, Emekah.

Emekah Sunny [*taking pause*]: Oh, oh … really?

Stacey: And I had your, your nub in a bag of ice …

Emekah Sunny: Oh.

> =.=
>
> =.=

So, so I guess y'all do know.

> =.=
>
> =.=

Y'all tried to help save me?

Stacey: Yes.

Emekah Sunny: =.=

Huh.

> =.=
>
> =.=

Y'all muthafuckas did a whack ass job of it!

> *Emekah / Sunny laughs.*
> *Sunny's breasts catch Emekah's eyes.*
> *Laughter subsides.*

Emekah ^{Sunny} [*re Sunny's breasts*]: Oooo, these are nice. Real nice … damn!

Emekah jiggles her chest.

Truth: Man, you betta keep them eyes glued to the wall
in front of you or—

Emekah ^{Sunny}: Or what?
What is wrong with you, Truth? A brotha cain't <u>look</u> no
more. <u>Lookin</u> is a crime, security man?

Suddenly, as if coming out of a deep sleep:

Sunny ^{Emekah}: Hello? He,he,hello?
=.= [*registering the ropes*]
What did y'all do to me? Why am I all—

Patricia: Sunny?

Sunny ^{Emekah}: Patricia! Why am I all tied up like this? Did I mess up the
outhouse?

Patricia: No, no. Listen to me Sunny: something … happened.

Sunny ^{Emekah}: To me?

Stacey: To you.

Patricia: That boy that died today …

Truth: Stacey and I got covered in his blood …

Patricia: And you got some of that in you …

Stacey: Got some of him in you …

Emekah ^{Sunny}: Got me all up in your gooshy shit!

Sunny ^{Emekah}: Who is that?

Patricia: That's what we tryin to tell you, Sunny—

Emekah ^{Sunny}: Sunny … that's a nice, juicy name—

Sunny screams.

Emekah ^{Sunny}: Shit, this girl can holler the skin offa a catfish—

Sunny screams.

Truth: Sunny. Sunny, now, now calm down. We gonna fix this—

Sunny: Is this what y'all do in this town? This why everybody wanted to
know who I was. This is what Wire meant when he was talkin about
an invasion—

Emekah covers Sunny's voice.

Emekah ^{Sunny}: I, I ain't very good at this body squattin.

I don't really know how to keep her quiet—AHHHHH!

That gurl den bit me—

Sunny ^{Emekah}: Patricia! Patricia! You got to help me—

Patricia: I will! We are!

Sunny and Emekah wrestle in Sunny's bod[y]
Her screams spin with his grunts. There's a
great big gasp from them both followed by
free-fall type yell then suddenly Sunny's bod[y]
goes limp.

Patricia: =.=

Stacey: =.=

Truth: =.=

Stacey: What the hell was that?

Truth: Sunny?! Sunny!

Patricia: Sounds like they fell from something—

Stacey: What could they fall from? The gurl's 5'3"!

Truth finds a mirror, crosses to Sunny's bod[y]
with a bit of caution. He reaches out and
holds a mirror under Sunny's nose.

Truth: She's still breathing.

Maybe we oughta let em stay out until Davis comes.

Stacey: Waymon Davis?

Truth: Uh-huh. I sent Wire for him.

Patricia: What is he gonna do about this?

Truth: He's gonna pull Emekah out of her.

Bring Sunny back to her senses.

Stacey: Since when does Waymon Davis handle lost souls?

Truth: Since Hunter Priestess died and he volunteered to make room for
her in his body.

She can come down in him, through him whenever she wants. Folks
got a soul to deal with, they call him and he channels her …

Stacey: For a fee though, right?

Truth: Of course but—

Patricia & Truth: I'll pay it.

They look at each other.

Truth: I'll pay it, Patty. Let me do it.

ricia [*backing down*]: Okay. Alright.

cey: I figure Davis don't care <u>who</u> the money comes from as long as it comes, right? Both of y'all can put in half. Everybody feels good about saving Sunny.

tricia: =.=

uth: =.=

tricia: No, no. That's alright. Truth says he'll pay. Let him pay.

acey: What's wrong with y'all?

tricia: Nuthin.

uth: Patricia and I just have a understanding …

tricia [*trying to cover her tracks*]: No understanding, Truth. You just said you want things to go down a certain way. And I respect that.

acey: Uh-uh. You don't respect nuthin
unless you get some benefit from it.

atricia: What are you gettin pinched up about, Stacey? Please dump your mistrust in the shit pot. There was some concern about method of payment and now it's smooth. Alright?

Truth exits the shop.

atricia: Where you goin?

ruth: That whiskey ran right through me.

Truth goes through Stacey's room onto the back porch down the steps. He's gone.

tacey: He got a bladder the size of a crock-pot. He don't have to pee. What are you hustlin him in to?

Patricia: Don't you get tired of snoopin?

tacey: =.=

Patricia: The brotha had to use the bathroom, Stacey. Ain't no more to it.

Stacey: =.= [*easing up*]

Patricia: =.= [*easing up*]

Stacey: =.=

Patricia sighs a genuine breath of exhaustion. Stacey looks at Patricia.

Stacey: =.=

=.=

You been takin care of yourself?

Patricia: Are you askin me how I been keepin?

Stacey: Whether you speak on it or not I know <u>how</u> you doin.

     I can feel you.

     I'm askin you if you takin care of yourself.

Patricia: You don't know a damn thing about me.

     Ain't how we do, remember?

Stacey: I know a lot of things.

Patricia: You don't know shit.

Stacey: I know Sunny's in love with you.

Patricia: What?

Stacey: =.=

Patricia: How you know that?

Stacey: She told me.

Patricia: When?

Stacey: On the porch. Earlier.

Patricia [*looking at Sunny's limp body*]: She loves me?

Stacey: She <u>thinks</u> she does.

Patricia: You don't think somebody could love me?

Stacey: =.=

Patricia: I can do other things besides pine.

     I can be *pined for*, Stacey.

Stacey: =.=

Patricia: =.=

> *Patricia crosses to Stacey's room.*

Stacey: Where you going?

Patricia: That whiskey hit me too. I'ma wait in line. Go in after Truth.

> *Patricia enters the back porch. She paces.*
>
> *In the shop, Stacey looks at Sunny's limp body.*
>
> *Truth steps up on the back porch. He sees Patricia:*

Truth: I didn't say anything, Patty. <u>Won't</u> say nuthin.

     I'm sorry. If somebody asks me a question, I cain't lie—

Patricia: I'm breakin the deal, Truth.

Truth: What? Why?

Patricia: I just cain't help you. I won't help you.

Truth: Tell me why?

Patricia: Cause …

Cause …

it ain't something I'm interested in doing anymore.

=.=

=.=

=.=

She loves me.

=.=

Sunny.

Truth: =.=

=.=

=.=

How you know that?

Patricia: She told Stacey.

Truth: How you know Stacey tellin the truth?

Patricia: He cain't lie about love.

He can <u>deny</u> it hella good but he cain't lie.

> *Truth exhales as this thought seeps into his mind.*

Truth: Well, well then I cain't help you no more either.

Patricia: I understand.

> *Truth slumps down, sits on the steps.*

Truth: =.=

=.=

=.=

I ain't got no plan c …

> *Patricia leans against the post.*

> *Wire jumps on the front porch, enters the shop, winded. His drum is slung over his shoulder.*

Wire: Where is Truth and Patty?

Stacey: Out back.

Wire [*re: Sunny*]: What happened to her?

Stacey: We don't know. She still breathin though … we gonna wait for Waymon Davis.

Wire: He's on his way. He told me to leave him alone so he could call Hunter Priestess.

Wire wipes his sweating brow with the back of his hand.
Stacey removes his handkerchief from his back pocket.

Wire: I think I lost it at that baby party. Sweatin is a part of my job. Truth told me to make it quick.

Stacey wipes Wire's face. It's a casual gestu *that quickly takes on an intimate and delicate tone.*

Stacey [*wiping Wire's brow*]: How did Waymon end up sharin his self with Hunter Priestess?

Through the following, Stacey wipes Wire *temples, his jaw line, under his chin, reache* *around wipes the back of his neck, behind his ears …*

Wire: Waymon was lonely.
He went to Hunter Priestess when she was alive to ask her to conjur him a lover. She did but he wasn't impressed. He had a high taste. H wanted more thighs, less butt, more brains, less poetics.
He wanted his money back.
They got to fighting about it. After the fighting came the talkin.
They found out they were soul mates.
=.=
She got skinned alive during the invasion. Died some hours later.
Waymon was devastated.
He went through her writings, learned how to call her to him.
And they came up with the present-day situation.
Stacey: Must needed her bad to make room for her like that.
Wire: Folks need people. That's the way life is.
Stacey: I know that first hand. You do, too.

=.=
=.=

Patricia enters Stacey's room. She's about to enter the shop but stops when she hears:

Stacey: I been back a week now and …

I, I don't know what to do now that the waitin's over.

You talkin bout waitin all those years …

All I know how to do with you is wait.

Been back here a week …

We finally got each other … and I'm clumsy.

Cain't settle in. Don't know how.

Wire takes Stacey's handkerchief. He places Stacey's hands on his chest / armor. The plastic crinkles.

Wire and Stacey breathe deep. Patricia, curious about this long moment of silence, peeks into the shop from the Stacey's bedroom. She looks in just as Stacey and Wire kiss.

Wire lets go of his drum. It crashes to the floor, but he remains connected to Stacey.

Immediately after they separate:

Stacey: Patricia needs to get …

Wire: … gone.

Patricia hears this and quietly steps away from the curtain. What is she going to do now?

Wire: We'll get Sunny right then they need …

Stacey: … to get gone.

Wire: They'll be alright on they own.

Stacey: More than alright. She's in love with her.

Wire: Who's in love with who?

Stacey [*gesturing to Sunny*]: She's in love with your sister.

Wire: Sunny tell you that?

Stacey: I could hear it in her voice.

Wire: Does Patty know?

Stacey: Uh-huh.

I told her.

Wire: You told her?

Stacey: Yea.

Wire: Why?

Stacey: Cause Truth was barkin about Sunny being his wife.

Sunny wasn't gonna be his wife.

Truth cain't be nobody's husband.

Wire: How you know?

Stacey: For a man like that ... love is tied up with owning things. He don't care who the woman is. He's just lookin to corner somebody.

Wire: And how is any of that your business?

Stacey: =.=

Wire: Why you tellin Patty what Sunny told you?

It ain't your business keepin Truth

from being somebody's husband—

Stacey: But it wasn't gonna happen—

Wire: Well if it wasn't gonna happen,

it means you don't need to meddle in it.

Stacey: Why you gettin all pinched at me?

Wire: 'Cause you kickin up dirt, stirrin pots that ain't yours—

Stacey: Pots that ain't mine? Patty and me been—

> *Patricia goes back to the curtain that leads to the shop.*

Wire: Don't talk that "you and Patty" shit, Stacey.

Stacey: You actin like I ain't got a right to—

Wire: You actin like a history with somebody gives you a right to hold on to em. It don't.

All that matters is who's got a hold of what's in here [*slaps his own chest, plastic crinkles*].

Stacey: And she ain't got a hold of that in me—

Wire: But you keepin a grip on hers.

Stacey: =.=

Wire: You been layin up with her while you was on the road?

Stacey: No.

=.=

=.=

She cain't function without some man tellin her how she is or how she oughta be. She held on to your daddy 'til she got too big for it then she moved on to you and then she ended up needing me. I'm the only man she got left. The only one that'll do right by her. She cain't do no better than me.

Wire: And you like that. Keepin that power over her?

Patricia pulls back the curtain. Steps into the shop.

Wire and Stacey look at her.

Patricia crosses over to Sunny. Holds a mirror under her nose. She's still breathing.

Stacey: Wire said Waymon Davis is coming.
    He's conjurin up Hunter Priestess then he'll be on his way.
Patricia: Uh-huh.
        =.=
        =.=

Wire takes Stacey's handkerchief and stuffs it in his pocket.

Wire [*to Stacey*]: You got a fresh shirt for me?
                I'm stinkin this one up ...
Patricia: There's a box of fresh clothes under his bed.
Stacey: =.=
Wire: =.=
Patricia [*to Stacey*]: Am I lying?
Stacey: Naw ...

Wire crosses into Stacey's room.
Takes off his shirt, grabs Stacey's handkerchief and wipes his back, armpits, around his armor. Stuffs it back into his pocket.

He finds one of Stacey's clean shirts.
In the shop, Patricia talks to Stacey but speaks loud enough so that Wire can hear her.

Patricia: I love my brother.
    He's scared of me though.
        =.=
    Can only do the big talk when I'm out of sight.
    Certain types of men is built that way ...

Wire reacts to this but remains silent.

Truth rises to his feet on the back porch. He enters Stacey's room.

Sees Wire.

He speaks quietly enough so that Wire is the
only one who can hear him.

Truth: Wire, Wire, I'm glad it's you.

Wire [*taken aback*]: Got-damn Truth. I forgot you was out there …

Truth: Look, I got something I need to talk to you about.

Stacey: You don't act like you love him.

Patricia: Neither did you until Truth told you

       you had to come stand in your daddy's shoes.

Truth: Do you need some extra help with your business?

Wire [*distracted*]: What?

Truth: Do you need help.

       I know how to drive—automatic and stick.

       Can swim a long ways.

       Learned hand-to-hand combat for the invasion.

       And you know I know how to keep things in order …

Stacey: You think I only came back cause this shop?

Patricia: I know you had your reasons, Stacey.

       Just like I got my reasons for comin back.

Stacey: You only got one reason, Patricia.

Patricia: And what is that?

Stacey: Me.

Patricia: You? [*Patricia laughs*] Negro, please.

Truth [*to Wire*]: I'm thinkin I might leave the shop.

       For good. Thinkin maybe I could work for you.

Patricia: You and Wire really think I need y'all, don't you?

Stacey: =.=

Patricia: I don't.

       I don't <u>need</u> anybody.

       Just choose to have people around me cause I like folks.

       And they like me.

Truth: I need you to seriously consider this, Wire.

Wire: Truth I ain't in the state of mind to consider anything right now.

Truth: I need to cut loose from all this.

       Got my soul busted too many times.

       But I cain't go to that factory …

Patricia: I came back for Wire's birthday.

       I came back to see how you were doin.

       And …

Wire steps out of Stacey's room wearing his shirt, carrying his handkerchief. Everyone, except Sunny, is dressed in Stacey's clothes.

Truth follows Wire. Patricia looks at him.

Patricia: I got a few gigs after I leave here, houses that want me not the act, so I cain't stay long …
It'd be nice to have some company.

Stacey: I'm sure Sunny'll go with you once we get her right.

Patricia: I'm sure she will.
But I'm talkin bout takin somebody who can maintain books, handle money, and other matters.
What you think about travelin around, Truth?

The whole room stops, eyes on Truth.

Truth: Travelin? With you?

Patricia: With me.

Stacey: You cain't be for real—

Patricia: Why not?

Truth: Why cain't she be?

Stacey [*to Truth*]: You cain't be serious bout goin?

Truth [*defiant*]: Why the hell not?

Wire: Stacey, maybe it's a good idea …

Stacey: What the hell kind of bullshit is y'all on? Truth cain't leave. He's in the papers. I'm about to own this shop which means I'm about to own hi—

Truth: You gonna own who?

Stacey [*backtracking*]: He'd be on the road with two women, he ain't even spent as much time with his own mama. He don't know how to act around women. Plus, plus he's in love with that girl. She ain't never gonna love him back.

Truth: Why do you care one way or the other?

Patricia: He don't.
He just cain't stand for you to be happy without him—

Stacey [*to Patricia*]: You cain't stand for me to have my shit together without you.

Patricia: What shit you got together? It took you a week to kiss Wire—

Wire [*to Patricia*]: You snoopin on me now, Patty?

Patricia: It's just a damn curtain up at that doorway. What you expect?

Truth: Ha! Busted!

       [*to Patricia*] You ain't gonna be in my business like that, are you Patty?

Patricia: You ain't got no business to speak of, so no.

Commotion. Patricia, Wire, Truth, and Stacey get wrapped up in a shouting match.

Insults spin from every mouth, confessions are made, truths are told but no one hears anybody cause everybody is cussing somebody out. Sunny's body remains limp.

Waymon Davis as Hunter Priestess climbs the steps onto the front porch, carrying a large carpenter's bag and tambourine. He wears a shirt stained with mud and dirt; worn workman boots and a soiled undershirt. Suspenders hold up his pants. He wears the clothes of a sharecropper. The purple haze that surrounds him is the only indication that he's carrying the skills needed to harness an unruly soul. He stands on the porch looking in at the chaos.

Waymon as Hunter Priestess puts down his bag and delivers a series of rolls with his tambourine.

Everyone continues to argue.

Waymon's rolls transform into a beat. It's a slow groove that snakes its way into the room and wraps around everyone's hips one-by-one. His flourish and dexterity with this instrument surprises those who have seen Waymon as Hunter Priestess play for the first time. This big, burly man can beat the tears out of the devil with the way he handles this thing.

Suddenly, Patricia, Wire, Truth, and Stacey emerge from their argument and start to sing a melody in time with the tambourine beat.

> *They enter a trance one-by-one until they have joined Waymon's soulful spin. Scat phrases mingles with words:*

Patricia & Truth & Stacey & Wire:
ooooooo, wah–wah, oooooooooo, doo–wah / Weeeeeeeee, wah–wah, ooooooo, wah–ah / da—da—da, la la / whoooooooooooooooooo is it? / whooooooooo is it? / hooooooooooooooo is it?

> *The four of them turn to Waymon Davis as High Priestess who continues to play. He enters the shop. Truth crosses out to the porch, brings Waymon's bag inside.*

Waymon as Hunter Priestess [*sung*]:
Children got a soul
they cain't set free!?

Patricia & Truth & Stacey & Wire [*sung*]:
Yeeeeeeessssss! Yea!
Yessssssssssssss!

> *The four of them sway, slide, and roll to Waymon as Hunter Priestess' beat.*

Waymon as Hunter Priestess [*sung*]:
Children got a soul they cain't set free?!

Patricia & Truth & Stacey & Wire [*sung*]:
Yeeeeeeessssss! Yea!
Yessssssssssssss!

Waymon as Hunter Priestess [*sung*]:
Send that soul to Hunter Priestess!
Send that soul straight unto me!
Send that soul to Hunter Priestess!
And that soul will soon be free!

> *They repeat the song again and again, improvising words, sounds, and feelings.*

Waymon as Hunter Priestess orchestrates t
brown bodies in the room with various tri
and rolls of his tambourine. An unconsciou
Sunny remains limp against the counter.
Patricia, Wire, Stacey and Truth sing and
clap, supporting Waymon's rhythm.

Waymon does one final trill just as Patricic
shuts off the lights in the shop and back roo
while turning on the Christmas / birthday
lights that line the front porch.

Waymon's purple haze settles against the
green haze that surrounds Sunny's body.
The sky is black, swallowing the pipes and
the smoke that seeps from them.

Everyone is silent. Only breath.

Patricia, Stacey, Truth, and Wire anchor
one side of the room.

Waymon as Hunter Priestess: Hey hey now.

The four of them stagger their responses.

Patricia: Hey hey …
Truth: Hey now hey …
Stacey: Hey now now …
Wire: Hey hey now …
Waymon as Hunter Priestess [*to Sunny's body*]: Emekah Evans!

The room waits.

Patricia, Truth, Stacey, and Wire get low to
the ground. They beat a quiet rhythm
against the floor.

Waymon pulls a small bottle of liquid from
the bib of his coveralls. He pops the top and
drinks the concoction. He plays a quiet
rhythm on the tambourine that serves as a

78

> *pace for him to walk with. He squats down right in Sunny's face and blows …*

> *Sunny snaps awake, gasping for air.*

> *Waymon shakes his tambourine.*

> *Sunny locks eyes with Waymon as Hunter Priestess.*

Sunny: =.= [*breathing*]

Waymon as Hunter Priestess: =.= [*looking*]

Sunny: Who, who are you?

Waymon as Hunter Priestess: You, my darling, are lookin at Mr. Waymon Davis. However, you're speakin with Mizzzzz Hunter Priestess. Now, who am I speakin with?

Sunny: This, this is Sunny talkin.

Waymon as Hunter Priestess: That's a pretty name, Sunny.

Sunny: Thank, thank you.

Waymon as Hunter Priestess: I got word you got company in there with you …

> *Frightened. Sunny nods. Waymon as Hunter Priestess caresses her face.*

Waymon as Hunter Priestess: Emekah?

> *Sunny nods.*

Waymon as Hunter Priestess: Where is he now, Sunny?

Sunny: He's passed out. Over in the corner of me. I can see the shape of 'em out the side of my eye …

Waymon as Hunter Priestess: That's how we want him. He's just as scared as you … don't know what he doin. A soul that don't know his powers yet is one that's easy to take down. You know what you can do for me?

Sunny: What?

Waymon as Hunter Priestess: If you look the other direction out the corner of your eye, you see that corner. It's empty, ain't it?

Sunny nods.

Waymon as Hunter Priestess: Crawl over in that corner and don't come out until I tell you to, alright?

Sunny: Okay.

=.=

=.=

Is Patricia still here?

> *Waymon as Hunter Priestess turns to the group. Patricia starts to say something.*

Waymon as Hunter Priestess: Don't say nuthin. Just let her see you.

> *Patricia raises up in Sunny's line of sight. Sunny smiles sheepishly. Sighs. Waymon as Hunter Priestess shoos Patricia down. Patricia gets back low. Reenters the riff.*

Waymon as Hunter Priestess: Now crawl over yonder in that corner Sunny, okay?

> *A series of sounds escape Sunny's body as she crawls to a corner in her body.*

Sunny [*in the distance*]: Okay.

> *Waymon as Hunter Priestess pulls another small bottle from his back pocket. He pops the top, drinks the concoction. He calls off the rhythm the group plays. Silence. Then he blows into Sunny's face again. Emekah wakes up. Gasps for air:*

Emekah Sunny: =.= [*breathing, wild-eyed*]

> *Waymon as Hunter Priestess shakes his tambourine.*

> *Emekah* Sunny *locks eyes with Waymon as Hunter Priestess.*

> *Emekah* Sunny *scoots back frightened.*

Waymon as Hunter Priestess: Hey hey now. Emekah.

Emekah ^{Sunny}**:** What the fuck is this shit!!? What you want?

Waymon as Hunter Priestess: Aww, now, you know what I want, Emekah.

Emekah ^{Sunny} [*yelling to the others*]**:** I told y'all I wanted my family! I want to go to my mama's house! Y'all den up and called Hunter Priestess and her, her man sack—

Waymon as Hunter Priestess: We callin folks out of their names? Is that how it is, Emekah?

Emekah ^{Sunny}**:** I want my people—

Waymon as Hunter Priestess: I heard about your accident, Emekah. Ivory told me it was gonna happen.

Emekah ^{Sunny}**:** She did?

Waymon as High Priestess nods.

Emekah ^{Sunny}**:** Where was she? Why'd she leave me hangin then?

Waymon as Hunter Priestess: I cain't answer that for you. Got to ask her yourself. Go to her and talk to her yourself.

Emekah ^{Sunny} [*shaking her head*]**:** I ain't leavin this girl, Priestess. Soon as I leave her no tellin where I end up. Only get one shot to make it to the ancestors. I already spoiled mine.

Waymon as Hunter Priestess: You cain't stay where you are, Emekah Evans.

Emekah ^{Sunny}**:** You cain't force me out.

Waymon as Hunter Priestess: What makes you think that?

Emekah ^{Sunny}**:** This lil body of brown sunshine. No scratches, nicks, or dents Mzzz Priestess. Gotta leave it how you found it. And I heard you don't do clean sweeps. Which means I'm stayin high and dry.

Waymon as Hunter Priestess: I usually don't do clean sweeps when I'm dealing with pricks. But you're a good boy, Emekah Evans.

Emekah ^{Sunny}**:** Don't call me boy.

Waymon as Hunter Priestess: You ain't gonna be a prick, are you boy?

Emekah ^{Sunny}**:** Well you actin like a cunt which means I'm bout to be a prick.

Waymon as Hunter Priestess stands up, steps back. This is going to be harder than anticipated …

Waymon as Hunter Priestess shakes his tambourine. Patricia, Truth, Wire and

*Stacey circle the room and barricade the
front door and the door leading to Stacey's
room.*

Truth and Stacey untie Sunny's body.

Emekah / Sunny springs to her feet and ru
*for the front door. Waymon as Hunter
Priestess catches Emekah / Sunny in mid-
air, spins her around and gently places the
body on the ground.*

*Emekah / Sunny drops low, rolls and
tumbles along the floor, trying to get to an
exit. With the shake of a tambourine
Patricia, Truth, Wire, and Stacey block
Emekah / Sunny at every roll and flip.*

Sunny springs to her feet. Winded. Stumped

Everyone in the room is ready to pounce.

*Suddenly, Waymon as Hunter Priestess
releases the tension by stepping back. He
walks casually over to his bag. The
tambourine goes down with great care. The
symbols hardly make a noise.*

Every pair of eyes watches him.

*He opens his bag. Pulls out a worn blanket
with abstract shapes in bold colors printed on
it. He places it on the ground. He pulls out a
portable stool and sets it on top of the
blanket.*

Waymon as Hunter Priestess: I'ma sit down here, Emekah Evans.
I'ma sit here.
And I'ma ask you some questions.

Emekah Sunny: I don't give a shit what you do.

Waymon as Hunter Priestess: =.=
=.=

*Waymon as Hunter Priestess removes a
pouch from his pocket. He places a pinch of*

82

powder on the back of his hand. Sniffs it up one nostril. Places another pinch on the back of his hand. Sniffs it up the other. He dumps the rest of the powder in his mouth. He mixes it up with his saliva. He swishes around his mouth. He swallows. He waits.

He exhales in Sunny's direction, surrounding her body in a purple haze. An invisible force shapes and shifts the body as if animated by a puppet master. Waymon as Hunter Priestess laughs. The force places Sunny on top the counter and places her in a very lady-like position—legs crossed, hands draped across the lap, head titled slightly to one side, a vapid expression rests on the face.

Patricia: What is she doin to her?!

Waymon as Hunter Priestess: She's a very pretty gal.
Mm-hm. She sho' nuff is ...

Emekah Sunny**:** You don't scare me a damn bit, Priestess.

Waymon as Hunter Priestess exhales in the body's direction. Sunny's body very slowly un-crosses her legs and sits wide-legged on the counter, gathering her skirt between her legs. The body leans towards Waymon as Hunter Priestess showing off its cleavage. A titillating sway back-and-forth, puts a smile on Waymon's face.

Waymon as Hunter Priestess: Ahhhhhhh …. [*laughs*]

Emekah Sunny**:** You think this shit is funny, bitch?

Waymon as Hunter Priestess: Oh, Emekah Evans, I seen you sit on the steps right outside this shop at holler at the gurl's who walked by …
Cain't blame me, can ya?

EmekahSunny**:** Ain't right for you to be doin it to another woman …

Waymon as Hunter Priestess: Waymon gave his body to me to wrestle with you. I ain't breakin your rules of how things supposed to work in this body, Emekahhhhhhh [*laughter*] ….

Truth: Ain't that enuff, Priestess?

Waymon as Hunter Priestess: Don't question me.

=.=

=.=

I know when it's enuff.

> *Sunny stops from raising her skirt, but continues to pose à la pin-up girl style, flashing a smile.*
>
> *Suddenly, Waymon as Hunter Priestess bangs his foot twice on the floor. Sunny's body returns to the lady-like pose.*
>
> *Sunny's body executes "lady-like" mannerisms and gestures as Emekah's voice bellows from the mouth.*
>
> *The following exchange is rapid fire:*

Waymon as Hunter Priestess: What do you consider a revolutionary act, Emekah Evans?

Emekah[Sunny]**:** What the fuck you talkin bout—

Waymon as Hunter Priestess: A revolutionary act, Emekah Evans. Name three.

Emekah[Sunny]**:** Fuck you.

Waymon as Hunter Priestess: That's one. You really want that to count as your first one?

Emekah[Sunny]**:** You tryin to psyche me out or some shit? I'm not leavin this body!

Waymon as Hunter Priestess: That's two. Fuckin me is one. Stayin in that body is two. What's three?

Emekah[Sunny]**:** This is a bunch of bullshit—

Waymon as Hunter Priestess: Disengagement. Very nice. Lazy but necessary. Fuckin me. Stayin in that body. And emotional detachment. Those are your revolutionary acts.

84

Emekah^{Sunny}: This is the muthafucka y'all called to deal with me? Crazy ass cat talkin about a revolutions?

Waymon as Hunter Priestess: Where were you during the invasion, Emekah Evans?

Emekah^{Sunny}: Where were you?

Waymon as Hunter Priestess: Waymon was strapped to a tree and whipped across the back 300 times while salt was poured on his wounds. I was forced to crack the whip. Pour that salt across his back. Where were you?

Emekah^{Sunny}: I was here.

Waymon as Hunter Priestess: Where.

Emekah^{Sunny}: With my people.

Waymon as Hunter Priestess: Locked up at your house.

Emekah^{Sunny}: So what?

Waymon as Hunter Priestess: So what!!!?
[*Sunny's body is locked in a lady-like position*]
The rest of the us was tryna fight to keep our town, but the Evans were a-wall. Deserters. Chicken-dick cowards.

Emekah^{Sunny}: Fuck you. We thought it was all over. The end of our people—

Waymon as Hunter Priestess [*mocking*]: Yea, yea, yea … you thought the invasion was when you people were gonna get pulled apart blah-blah-blah.

Emekah^{Sunny}: Don't "blah-blah" that shit man. We thought it was over.

Waymon as Hunter Priestess: Sittin in your cul-de-sac shacks, the Evans clan thought the prophecy was gonna be fulfilled.

Emekah^{Sunny}: You a heartless skank—

Waymon as Hunter Priestess: So your 4th revolutionary act is sittin in your house on your goddamn ass until y'all got the all clear—

Emekah^{Sunny}: You can suck my dick, Hunter Priestess.

Waymon as Hunter Priestess: Right after you grow some balls, young blood.

Emekah^{Sunny}: You wanna see what I'm packin?

Waymon as Hunter Priestess: Waymon is packin a bigger sack than you and every other damn man in that Evan's clan. Lettin some woman curse your line.

Emekah^{Sunny}: She ain't "some woman!"

Elder Ivory Evans was the start of our line—

Waymon as Hunter Priestess: She was sick—

Emekah^{Sunny}: Shut up!!

Waymon as Hunter Priestess: Twisted in the head like a white man chasin brown tail—

Emekah^{Sunny}: SHUT UP!

Waymon as Hunter Priestess: Heard voices.

Emekah^{Sunny}: She had visions!

Waymon as Hunter Priestess: Boogie man pullin at her skirt.

Emekah^{Sunny}: Got harassed for being redbone—

Waymon as Hunter Priestess: Kept scratchin at the veins in her wrists.

Emekah^{Sunny}: She's takin us to the promise land.

Waymon as Hunter Priestess: Wasn't no name for what she had back then but we all know what it is now. We know it, and we can name it … 'cept y'all Evans a lil bit sensitive about it—

Sunny's body begins to shake, but the head remains still. Emekah is full of rage that bubbles out of the pores of Sunny's skin.

Emekah^{Sunny}: You dirty raggedy piece of shit! Talkin about my people … talkin bought Ivory … you don't know shit about my people … she wasn't crazy … <u>we</u> ain't crazy. They, they, they made her that way. Made us this way … you, you talkin out your, your stank ass Hunter Priestess.

Waymon as Hunter Priestess: Uh-uh. Emekah Evans. Everybody know'd Ivory was sick in the head.

Waymon as Hunter Priestess turns to Patricia, Wire, Truth, Stacey.

Emekah doesn't hear this because he's steeped in such rage.

Waymon as Hunter Priestess [*hushed*]: Cover your eyes. Close your ears when I say the word. He's gonna come after me then try to hide in one of y'all.

Emekah^{Sunny}: Dried up piece of pig dick ... stupid tar baby ... black ignorant ... piece of fuckin ... you don't know my people ... she wasn't crazy ... they, they made her that way. Made us that way. They was tryin to kill us off ... tried killing all of us.

Waymon as Hunter Priestess: =.=

=.=

=.= *[watching the body shake]*
She was a, a ... para.noid schizo.phrenic, ain't that right Emek—

> *The spirit of Emekah Evans shoots out the bottom of Sunny's feet. It ricochets across the room. Sunny's body falls limp, passed out on the counter.*

Waymon as Hunter Priestess [*yells to Patricia, Stacey, Truth, Wire*]: Close EM UP!

> *The four of them cup their ears and close their eyes. A dark shadow bursts past Waymon knockin him off his stool. Waymon wails as if being punched and kicked.*
>
> *A blur as Emekah's soul tries to find another body to crawl into, but Patricia, Stacey, Wire and Truth are shut tight.*
>
> *Objects are knocked around, thrown across the space as Emekah blindly searches for a way to survive.*
>
> *He goes to Sunny, her body shakes but she's locked up, too.*
>
> *Waymon crawls to his tambourine. Grabs it and shakes a long trill.*
>
> *Waymon as Hunter Priestess plays a series of staccato jabs with the tambourine.*
>
> *Emekah's spirit spins and spins and spins, arms flailing in a violent manner. Pats himself as if putting out a fire all over his body. Holds his hands up to the heavens, reaching, reaching. Jumps. Jumps. Jumps as*

*if trying to get at the only fruit on the
highest limb. On the final jump a roar
erupts from him and Emekah's soul
disappears.*
*The air is still. The sky is grey. No smoke
from the factory pipes.*

FOUR.

Dawn the following morning.
*The shop is still a mess from Emekah's
furious eruption.*

*Patricia and Sunny are in Stacey's bed.
Patricia holds Sunny and gently caresses her.
Sunny breathes deep, having a fitful sleep.*

*In the shop, Truth, Wire and Stacey sleep on
the floor. Stacey holds Wire who sleeps deep.
The men stopped responding to Sunny's
whimpers hours ago.*

*Waymon climbs the steps onto the back porch,
carrying a basin of fresh water.*

*His wears an undershirt. His dress shirt, still
tucked in his pants, hangs around his waist.
He places the basin on a pedestal, splashes his
face and the back of his neck.*

*He takes several deep breaths. Dries his face
and neck on a towel. He enters Stacey's room.*

Patricia looks at him.

*Waymon is meek and mild mannered. He's
nothing like the person who stepped on the
front porch earlier as Hunter Priestess.*

Waymon: =.=
Patricia: =.=
Sunny: =.= *[whimpers in her sleep]*

Waymon: She'll be alright.

It's just the residue.

She's gotta work through it.

Waymon places a bottle on the writing table.

Waymon: Rub some of this on her lips.

And just under her nose every four hours.

It'll help flush it out faster.

=.=

=.=

=.=

Hunter Priestess says y'all be fine together.

=.=

=.=

And she apologizes if she got outta hand.

=.=

=.=

A part of the job.

Patricia: Thank you Waymon.

Waymon nods, enters the shop. Stacey wakes up at the sound of his footsteps.

Stacey: You want a fresh shirt?

Waymon: Naw, I'ma be alright.

The air'll do me good.

Priestess can choke me up sometimes.

Feels good to be loose when she lets go of me.

Truth snaps awake. Looks around. Sees Waymon.

Truth: Waymon?

Waymon: Yea, it's me. Priestess let me loose.

Truth: Alright …

Truth climbs to his feet. He digs for his wallet, pulls money from it, gives it to Waymond.

Truth: That it?

Waymon counts it.

Waymon: That's it.

The men shake hands.

Truth: Priestess don't play.
Waymon: No she don't.
Cain't do without her though.
=.=
=.= [*starts packing up his things*]
[*to Truth*] Hey, hey, you goin home?
I can walk back yonder with you.
Truth: Yea, yea. I just need a minute …

Truth crosses into Stacey's bedroom.
Stacey watches him. Looks at the curtain.

Stacey [*to Waymon*]: You hungry?
We got some cereal 'round here …
[*taking in the mess*] somewhere …

Truth stands before Sunny and Patricia.

Truth: How's she doin?
Patricia: She ain't no worse.
Waymond gave me something to help her.
Truth: Good.
=.=
Patty, I'm acceptin your offer. Is it still on the table?
Patricia: It is.
But you gotta be sure you're comin with me for the right reasons,
though. Don't do it to piss off Stacey or keep tabs on Sunny.
Truth: It's for me. I'ma try doin this for myself.
After Hunter Priestess freed Sunny,
I felt like I got free, too.
My small way of thinkin, bein, got pulled out of me, too.
And goin overseas is something I never thought I'd do.
Patricia: Well overseas probably won't happen for a while.
No duo, no foreign lands.
I'm a solo act now which means starting back at the bottom.
Truth: That's alright. That's fine.
We'll get you over them seas soon enough.

> *A whimper seeps from Sunny that's a bit edgier than what we've heard.*

Patricia: Hand me that bottle on the table.

> *Truth gives the small bottle to Patrica. She unscrews the top, dabs some of the potion on her finger and intimately, delicately wipes it on Sunny's lips, just under her nose.*
>
> *Truth quietly exits the bedroom, enters the shop.*

Waymon [*to Stacey*]: Order some sage and burn it all over, everywhere … chase any and everything out.

Stacey: I'll do that first thing.

Truth: I'll be back by to help clean up. Need to be in my own clothes, sleep in my own bed.

Stacey: Alright … What about when Patricia and Sunny leave? You gonna be around then?

Truth: No.

Stacey: =.=

Truth: Ain't nobody here for me, Stacey.

> *Truth puts on his shoes. Grabs his bag. Waymon grabs his bag. The two men step out the front door, climb down the front steps.*
>
> *They're gone.*
>
> *Stacey looks down at Wire. Looks back at the curtain to his bedroom. Looks around the shop.*

Stacey [*to Patricia*]: Did you hear that? He said, "ain't nobody here for me."

Patricia [*holding Sunny*]: I can understand that.

> *Patricia wipes Sunny's brow. Sunny slowly opens her eyes, looks up at Patricia.*

When it registers who's holding her, Sunny kisses Patricia.

Immediately after they separate:

Patricia: Stacey, I'm gonna be fine without you.

Sunny closes her eyes. Snuggles up to Patricia.

Stacey: Okay, Patricia.
Patricia: You don't believe me?
Stacey: Truth'll be good for you.
Patricia: Truth'll be good for his self.
Stacey: =.=
Patricia: =.=
Stacey: Patricia …

Patricia …
Patricia: Hm?
Stacey: =.=

=.=
Patricia: What is it Stacey?

Stacey begins the opening of their comedy routine.

Stacey: Tell the people how you feelin this evening …
Patricia [*not getting it*]: What?
Stacey: We rode all the way here to this lovely county,

let these people know how to feelin tonight …
Patricia [*a slow realization*]: Oh …

Oh …

Oh …

For real, Stacey?
Stacey: For real. Just for now. This moment.
Patricia [*performing the routine*]: Well, Stacey I'ma have to be real with 'em.

I gotta be real wit y'all tonight.
Stacey: Gone 'head and tell em.

I shouldn't be the only one who's sufferin …
Patricia: It's that time of the month, ladies.

Y'all know what I'm sayin'.

And Stacey don't wanna help a sista when she wrestlin wit some fierce pussy demons.

Stacey: Uh-uh. No. No.

You got to fight the good fight on your own …

No way, Jack, I will see you on the other side of next week, you feelin me?

Patricia: See? But I do get mean around this time. I do. Don't I, Stacey?

Stacey: She does.

Patricia: I do. Mm-hm. Get so mean I make milk curdle. Get so mean I throw a drownin man both ends of the rope. So mean I have dreams I died and would wake up from the heat …

> *Blue smoke starts to pump out of the factory pipes.*
>
> *The work whistle blows in the distance to signify the start of another workday.*
>
> *The sun blossoms a bright orange like a bowl of fruit in the sky.*

Stacey: =.= [*holds Wire*]
Wire: =.= [*sleeps*]
Patricia: =.= [*holds Sunny*]
Sunny: =.= [*sleeps*]

> *As lights fade:*

Stacey: Ladies and gentlemen, I got a song I'd like to dedicate to Ms. Patricia tonight.

Patricia: What you gonna sing for me?

> *Stacey sings* "Happy Birthday" *to Patricia. It is a genuine, soulful performance*

Patricia [*touched, but covers it*]: You got some nerve talkin bout birthdays, boy ….

end of play.

HOW TO CATCH CREATION

Players:

>Griffin – late 40s
>Tami – early 40s
>Riley – late 20s
>Stokes – late 20s
>
>G.K. Marche (pronounced "mar-shay") – early 30s; early 80s
>Natalie – early 30s; early 50s
>
>All characters are Black American

Time:

>2014, and 1966, 1967. There's a brief moment in 1988.

Place:

>A place that resembles San Francisco and surrounding areas.

Note:

>The pace is swift, effortless ... the humor is alive and well ...   and so is the love.

...mi sits with Griffin in his apartment.

Griffin.
I think I want to have a kid.

Tami
=.=

Griffin.
Did you hear what I said?
=.=
=.=
I think I want a kid.
=.=
I sit on the train, and I smile at babies,
and they always smile back at me.
=.=
Even when I was a young man that always happened to me.
I would ride the train, mind my own business,
read the paper, or a book,
and then a baby would tug at my pages, or call out to me—
'Hi!'
'Hi!'
I look up and there's a round, brown, chubby-cheeked face
smiling at me.
=.=
=.=
I want a kid.

Tami.
It's about more than smiling at them—having a kid.
You just can't smile at it for 18 years.

Griffin.
I know that.

Tami.
Raising a kid takes longer than a train ride across
the bridge.

Griffin.
I know that.

Tami.
You shouldn't smile at random kids.

Griffin.
It's not a crime.

Tami.
It's a social one.
A social crime.

Griffin.
A smile is a crime?

Tami.
If that smile is surrounded by
a beard, broad shoulders, and big hands—yes.

Griffin.
Just because I'm a man—

Tami.
Yes—

Griffin.
Means I shouldn't smile at children.

Tami.
If I had my kid on the train,
and you smiled at my kid
=.= [*lawd have mercy*]
You just shouldn't do it.

Griffin.
If you have a kid,
and *if* I see the two of you on the train,
I won't smile.

Tami.
=.=

Griffin.
=.=

Tami.
=.=

Griffin.
Why are you so negative?

Tami.
I'm a realist.

Griffin.
The glass is always half empty with you.
Hairline cracks that you don't notice until
it's already filled with drink.

Tami.
I'm a realist.
I have a tv. I read the paper.
I watch the news. I talk to educated people.

Griffin.
You're a pessimist.

Tami.
=.=

Griffin.
=.=

Tami.
I worry about you smiling at kids.

Griffin.
=.=

Tami.
It's not a smart thing to do.
People don't trust men
who are nice to kids they don't know.
=.=
Creeps and pervs ruined it for good men.
=.=
You're a good man.
But those parents don't know that.
So when you smile …

Griffin.
I get it…

Tami.
Just be careful.

Griffin.
=.=

Tami.
=.=

Griffin.
You really think I'm a good man?

Tami.
=.=

Griffin.
=.=

Tami.
They know you have a good heart, those kids.
A warm heart can make a person smile.

Griffin.
=.=

Tami.
Do you really think I'm negative?

Griffin.
I tell you I want a kid.
You call me a pervert.

Tami.
Way to edit the conversation, Griffin.

Griffin.
Well …

Tami.
=.=

Griffin.
=.=

Tami.
You want a boy or a girl?

Griffin.
As long as it's healthy.

Tami.
=.=

Griffin.
=.=

Tami.
You'll be 65 when the kid goes to college.

Griffin.
=.=

Tami.
You'll be in your 80s when they finish their PhD.
You'll be dead by the time they get tenure.

Griffin.
Why is my kid a professor?

Tami.
No good?

Griffin.
A professor of what?

Tami.
Race and multi-media politics in a dystopian society.

Griffin.
Is that a degree?
Can a person get tenure with that knowledge?

Tami.
Your kid designed their own degree.
A cross-disciplinary exploration.
Groundbreaking.

Griffin.
They got it like that?

Tami.
They got it like that.
But you'll be dead.
So you'll never see it.

Griffin.
You'll have to witness it for me.

Tami.
I'll make sure it's a big celebration.
Cocktails. Suits. Pocket squares. Dresses. Heels.
Everyone gathered to praise your child.

Griffin.
I'll write speeches before I cross over.
You can read them at each celebration—
graduation, tenure, wedding reception, the first child, the second, the
third.
Read each one out loud. Don't just let them read it.
It's important for the kid to hear the praise.

Tami.
I will.

Griffin.
But I won't be dead.
I'll try not to be dead.
=.=
Unless I have to.

Tami.
=.=

Griffin.
Morbid conversation.
This is what I'm talking about—the negativity.
I don't even have a kid, but we're talking about
me being dead by graduation.

Tami.
Tenure, not graduation.

Griffin.
=.=

Tami.
=.=

Griffin.
=.=

Tami.
You know you need help, right?

Griffin.
Help?

Tami.
With the kid.

Griffin.
What kind of help?

Tami.
Creating it.

Griffin.
Are you offering?

Tami.
No I am not—

Griffin.
Because it sounds like you are—

Tami.
I said I'd read your speeches.
I'd throw the kid at least three different parties.
I agree to be in its life, but my duties stop at any fluid exchange.

Griffin.
You make it sound so romantic.

Tami.
Are you …?
You're not dating anybody.

Griffin.
=.=

Tami.
Are you?

Griffin.
=.=

Tami.
Are you smashing anybody?

Griffin.
Why do you say that word?

Tami.
Are you?

Griffin.
That's a terrible word.

Tami.
Answer my question.

Griffin.
I don't 'smash.'
So: no.

Tami.
The sex part is a significant step to have a kid.

Griffin.
That's some backwards thinking.

Tami.
You do know where babies come from?

Griffin.
Tami …

Tami.
You didn't forget, did you?

Griffin.
People have babies in all sorts of ways.
It's 2014.
If you have the money, you can have a kid.

Tami.
Well, you have the money.

Griffin.
Some money.
Not enough.

Tami.
What type of creation are you trying to buy?

Griffin.
I just started looking into it.

Tami.
Seriously?

Griffin.
Yes.

Tami.
Are you for real considering this?

Griffin.
Yes, Tami.

Tami.
Shit.

Griffin.
I wouldn't just…

Tami.
I thought you were just …

Griffin.
I'm not.
I'm for real about this.

Tami.
Damn …

Griffin.
=.=

Tami.
=.=

Griffin.
It's all I think about lately.
I want to make it happen.

Tami.
=.=
Wow …

Griffin.
That's all you're saying?

Tami.
Fuck …

Griffin.
Whatever, Tami.
This is why I pick and choose what I tell you.

Tami.
And you choose to tell me the real shit,
because you know I'll tell you the real shit.

Griffin.
So tell me the real shit.
Something other than: damn, shit, fuck, and wow.

Tami.
=.=
=.=
You have a beautiful heart.

Griffin.
=.=

Tami.
You would be a wonderful father.

2.

Stokes and Riley's apartment.
Stokes enters carrying a worn box. Riley follows.

Stokes.
Thank you for opening the door, babe.
Cuz once I put this box down, I ain't picking it back up…

He places it on the floor. A bit winded.

Riley.
[*playful*]
You letting a box full of books
and two flights of stairs skool like that you, son?

He grabs Riley, kisses her. She smiles.

Stokes.
I gotta get back in the gym.

Riley.
I'll schedule the rematch.
Stokes vs. paperbacks: the flight of the century.

Stokes.
Jokes! You got jokes.
This … this is new for you …

A bit of playful wrestling to which Riley immediately calls:

Riley.
Truce! Truce …!

They settle down.

Stokes.
These books are in pretty good condition. See?

Stokes reveals a few and hands them to Riley. She skims them.

Stokes.
The spines are hardly creased on most of 'em.

Riley.
Where'd you find these?

Stokes.
Street sale. I was killing time on my lunch break.
That whole box was only a few bucks.

Stokes. (continued)
Mostly novels, a few short story collections.
All by the same author.

Riley.
[*reads*]
"G.K. Marche"…?

Stokes.
Yea, a Black woman.
The older books were published in the late 60s.
Maybe I can sell 'em on eBay.
You check the mail?

Riley.
No. You sure you're able to?

Stokes.
Yo, you keep cracking on me … that box is for real heavy.
There are some hardcovers in there.

Stokes exits to the mailbox.
Riley keeps one book, tosses the others in the box.

Riley.
[*reads the back cover*]
"A singular voice that explores the revolutionary act
of Black intimacy in a climate of Black rage…"
[*to herself*]
What does <u>that</u> mean …?

Riley flips to a random page. Reads silently for a few moments. Flips randomly again.

Riley.
[*reads*]
"… doubt followed each breath.
She searched her dark skin for the fire that crackled just below the
surface,
but discovered only traces of smoke within—no passion, no fight.
She was a young woman filled with smoldering ash."

Stokes returns, flips through a stack of mail, searching.

Riley.
Miss G.K. seems like an upbeat lady …

Stokes spots a familiar return address. He opens the envelope. Skims.
His face falls. Riley looks to him.

Riley.
Stokes … ?

Without saying a word he hands her the letter. Riley skims. He turns his attention to
the box, retrieves a book at random.

Riley's read enough.

Riley.
I'm sorry.

Stokes.
Another one for the rejection pile.

Riley.
The idiot pile.

Stokes.
Thirteen schools can't be idiots.

Riley.
Says who?

Stokes.
Logic.
There's a higher probability that my paintings just suck.
Maybe I'm the fool for painting portraits of the same Black man.

Riley.
Your father.
You paint his face; you paint yours.
You have your father's face.
You paint the link between father and son.

Stokes.
And who wants to see that over and over?

Riley.
Everyone. Very, very soon.
Everyone will line up to see the power in that.

Riley kisses Stokes lovingly on the brow or cheek.

Riley.
I'm proud of you. I'm proud of the work you create.

Stokes.
Even if I suck at it?

Riley.
You don't suck. They suck.
You, you are fan-fucking-tastic.

Stokes kisses Riley. A moment of comfort between the lovers. Stokes's mind wanders ... he flips through one of G.K.'s books.

Stokes.
... maybe I should try something else.
Maybe I need a break from the portraits.

Riley.
You shouldn't let these schools make you doubt yourself, Stokes.

Stokes.
I'm not, babe.
I just ... it's just a thought.
[*he returns to the book, reads*]
Chapter One: The First Ring ...

3.

Alone in his apartment, Griffin paces. He's more hype than nervous. Before he makes an important phone call he rehearses the conversation from his end.

Griffin.
Ring, ring. Ring, ring.
"Yes, hello. How are you this afternoon?
Good, good. My name is Griffin B. Charles.
I would like to schedule a consultation
with Mrs. Newton. My research about her
says she provides legal services for independent adoption as well as
surrogacy.
And I would like to explore my options in both areas."
=.=
Alright. That should be fine.
Let's do this.

Griffin makes the call. We hear the phone ring from his end.

Then:

Receptionist.
Good afternoon, Newton and Bayles Law Office.
How may I help you?

Griffin.
=.= [*unable to speak*]

Receptionist.
Hello?

Griffin.
=.= [*still unable*]

Receptionist.
Is anyone there?

We hear a click. Call ended.
Griffin slowly removes the phone from his ear.

4.

Riley stands in Tami's office.

Riley.
Hi.

Tami.
Hello.

Riley.
=.=

Tami.
=.=
=.=
Do you need something?

Riley.
Yes.
I'm looking for Tami Sterling-Brown …?

Tami.
That's me.

Riley.
Oh.

Tami.
What do you need?

Riley.
Oh.
=.=
I didn't think you'd be …

Tami.
Be what?

Riley.
I saw your face online.
In a few group pictures.
But I didn't think the Director of Painting
would be … you.

Tami.

What is this about?

Riley.

I want to talk to you about a student.

Tami.

You're a parent?

Riley.

Excuse me?

Tami.

You have a child enrolled here at the conservatory?

Riley.

Oh! No no no no no no …
No. I'm only …

Tami.

I was about to say …
You look too young to …

Riley.

Baby free since '87.

Tami.

???

Riley.

That was the year I was born.

Tami.

Oh.

Riley.

It was a way for me to say: I don't have any kids.

Tami.
Right.
=.=
So, you're here for a student.

Riley.
Yes.
Stokes Michelle.

Tami.
And what year is he?

Riley.
Well, see, he's not.
He isn't enrolled here.

Tami.
You said he was a student.

Riley.
He was rejected from the MFA Painting program.
But he should've been accepted.

Tami.
Oh…

Riley.
I was wondering if you could …

Tami.
Oh, I see what's happening…

Riley.
… maybe tell me why you
didn't accept him.

Tami.
Well, Miss … ?

Riley.
Riley is fine.

Tami.

I'm not permitted to offer
feedback to applicants who were turned down, Miss Riley.

Riley.

You're not giving direct feedback. Not really.
He didn't send me. He doesn't know I'm here.
It's ... He applied to 14 schools this year.
He's been rejected by 13.
And I think it's effecting his self—

Tami.

I'm sorry, but—

Riley.

Whatever you think is missing in his work,
I can guarantee he's willing to find it.
If he could just be in a program, spend the time to examine his
work...
I know he's willing to find whatever's missing.

Tami.

Are you in school?

Riley.

No. Why?

Tami.

You're still carrying that grad student energy ...

Riley.

I graduated two years ago.
And this is woman-on-a-mission energy,
nothing to do with grad school ...

Tami. [*interest piqued*]
Two years ago from where?

Riley.

Santa Clarion.

Tami.
What did you study?

Riley.
Masters in computer science.

Tami.
[*surprised*]
Really?

Riley.
I don't like that.
People always react like that.

Tami.
Like what?

Riley.
Surprised. By my degree.
What degree do I look like I should have?

Tami.
Why do you think people are surprised?

Riley.
Because I'm Black.
Because I'm a woman.
Because I'm queer.
I'm sociable. I bathe.
My hair looks like this.
I talk like this.
I carry this bag.
Wear these clothes. These shoes.
Because my boyfriend is a painter.

Tami.
The list is long.

Riley.
It is.

Tami.
You reacted to me in the same way.

Riley.
Excuse me?

Tami.
Just now.
When you walked in you didn't expect the
brown face you saw in those group photos online, to be
the Director of Painting at the Francisco Bay Art Conservatory.

Riley.
=.=

Tami.
Who did you think Tami Sterling-Brown would be?
The red head? The blonde? The brunette wearing the horn-rimmed
glasses?

Riley.
=.=

Tami.
Any of them. But not me.
=.=
Santa Clarion has a solid CS program.

Riley.
It's not that I thought a Black woman couldn't
run this program.
I just assumed the person who rejected Stokes
would be the red head, the brunette—

Tami.
There's a committee.

Riley.
I know, but …

Tami.
A small group of highly qualified practitioners
who examine the quality of the work as well as the potential.

Riley.
So what exactly is Stokes missing?
Quality or potential?

Tami.
How did you even get in this building?
You need a key card...

Riley.
A brotha let me in downstairs.
I can show you Stokes's work right now.
I have pics on my phone.

Riley retrieves her phone, taps and swipes towards Stokes's paintings.

Riley.
Just look at them
and …

Tami.
=.=

Riley.
I don't need this to be an analytic deconstruction.
I just want advice. Something that can help him.
He asks me what I think of his work.
If you tell me your thoughts, I can maybe sneak a few
of your words into mine. See how he reacts.
Maybe he can find what's missing.
So that when he applies again, there will be more
where there used to be less.

Riley holds out her phone for Tami to take it.

Riley.
Miss Sterling-Brown, please.

A look between the two women.
A moment of something … more flashes.

Riley.
=.=

Tami.
=.=
=.=

Tami takes Riley's phone. Their hands touch during the exchange. And while both women feel the charge of that touch, they play it off as quickly as it happened.

Riley.
Swipe to the left.

Tami swipes.

Tami.
Oh yes … I remember this work.

She swipes, considers for a moment, swipes again.
Swipes, swipes, swi—

She hands the phone back to Riley.

Tami.
Tell him to let go.

Riley.
Let go of what?

Tami.
He's trying too hard to remember everything.
He's straining to achieve accuracy.
He should paint from sensation, emotion, desire.
When Mr. Michelle asks you what you think, tell him: let go.
=.=
His work is decent.

Riley.

You couldn't put him on the wait-list?

Tami.

The pool was strong this year. It is every year.
He has to be ready to do real work, real exploration.

Riley.

This is the only local program he applied to.

Tami.

What's next for you?
Google? Twitter? Microsoft?

Riley.

No.

Tami.

No?
The Google cafeteria is fantastic.
A colleague of mine works there.

Riley.

I'm waiting to see where Stokes ends up.

Tami.

Yes, but what about you?
Where do you want to go?

Riley.

I want to stay. Here.
=.=
I want to make something happen here.
=.=
But he wants a deeper commitment to a creative passion.
And he's willing to go anywhere to find it.
I don't want to leave. I don't want him to leave.
This is why I needed to hear you say
why you didn't accept him.

Tami.
=.=

Riley.
=.=

Tami.
You should stay.
If it's what you want.
Stay here.
=.=
Tell him: let go.
I tell you: stay.

5.

Split scene.
In 2014, Stokes reads one of G.K. Marche's novels.
In 1966, G.K. Marche edits the novel that Stokes reads.

Riley enters.

Riley.
Hey.

Stokes.
[*reads*]
Hey.

Natalie enters.

Natalie.
Hi.

G.K.
Hi…

          Natalie.
          What are you working on?

          G.K.
          Edits. Dark Sight.

Riley.
What are you reading?

Stokes.
Dark Sight.

Natalie.
[*playful; sincere*]
The highly anticipated debut novel of
1966 written by … [*kisses G.K.'s cheeks*]

Riley.
…that G.K. Marche lady?

Stokes.
Yup.

Riley.
How is it?

Natalie.
… going?

Stokes.
Great!

G.K.
Eh.

Riley.
Good.
=.= [*kiss*]
I'll read it after you
finish.
What do you want
for dinner?

Natalie.
Okay…
I'm sure it's better
than you think.
=.=
What do you want
for dinner?

Stokes.
Not hungry.

G.K.
Not hungry.

Riley.
Alright …
Maybe I'll order
something later.

Natalie.
Alright …

Riley exits.

Natalie.
[*flirtatious*]
Do you think you'll have
any particular cravings later?

G.K.
[*slight annoyance*]
I'm trying to rewrite this chapter,
Natalie.

Natalie.
Okay…
=.=
Maybe I'll make some soup later…

Natalie exits.

In 2014, Stokes reads one of G.K. Marche's novels.
In 1966, G.K.Marche edits the novel that Stokes reads.

For several beats, their movements, shifts, coughs are synchronized.
The moments of unison morphs into a duet of concentration, the engrossed.

Stokes and G.K. settle into an intimate stillness.

6.

Tami.
Here.

Griffin.
What's this?

Tami.
Read the cover.

Griffin.
[*reads*]
"The Side Streets Called Home:
An Exploration (!!!) of America's Slums" (!!!) How did you …?

Tami.
That's a review copy. A colleague finished his.
Said I could have it. So it's yours.

Griffin.
This isn't supposed to come out for months!
I can use this in my guest lecture.

Tami.
Where?

Griffin.
Daymont College.

Tami.
Why won't you let me find you a permanent teaching position?
I could negotiate a nice contract for you.
You've been doing the college circuit for a year.

Griffin.
It's a nice way to see the country.
A chance I missed when I was younger.
What are you drinking? Red or white?

Tami.
Just a bit of white. I'm driving.

Griffin goes to the kitchen to pour wine.

Tami spots a shopping bag—curious she peeks inside.

Griffin.
How was your day?

Tami.
[*while snooping*]
The usual.
Except for an unexpected visit from …

Tami pulls out a garment from the bag.

It's a gender-neutral onesie with stars and sleeping moon printed on the front. Tami is surprised (?), confused (?), concerned (?).

Griffin.
An unexpected visit from who?

Tami pulls out other things from the bag.
Booties, a bright-colored jumper with smiling balloons stitched on it.

Griffin.
Tami ...?

Tami holds the clothes in her arms when Griffin walks in carrying two glasses of wine.

Tami.
=.=

Griffin.
=.=

Tami.
What the fuck, Griffin?

Griffin.
=.= [sets down the glasses]

Tami.
This onesie costs fifty dollars.

Griffin crosses over and takes the clothes from her.
He put everything back in the bag.

Griffin.
I'm not embarrassed.

Tami.
I never said you should be.
You should feel obligated—

Griffin.
To do what?

Tami.
To explain why you have a bag full of
baby clothes and no baby.

Griffin.
I went to a place earlier today.
They were having a sale—

Tami.
Fifty dollars is the sale price?!

Griffin.
I just wanted to browse.
Then … the sales woman started following me. Casually.
And then she asks, "are we looking for anything special today?"
And before I thought twice about it, I said, "yes...a little one is on the
way."
She asked, "Is it a boy or girl?"
And I tell her, "As long as it's healthy."
And she smiled at me.
A for-real smile, not out of suspicion or uneasiness, then she
congratulated me.
We spent twenty minutes picking out baby clothes.
$346 later, I came home with this bag.
I'll return it.
I have 30 days to return it.
I hadn't unpacked it, because I'm going to return everything.

Tami.
Are you?

Griffin.
=.=
=.=
Drink your wine.

Tami.
I don't want it.

Griffin.
I want to toast your gift.
The book.

Tami.
I lost the taste for it.

Griffin.
You act like I got a body in that bag.
It's just a pile of hope in there.
I want to toast you looking out for me.

Tami.
=.=

Griffin.
=.=

Tami.
=.=

Tami takes the glass.

Tami.
I cave all the damn time.
I fold when I know it's a mistake.

Glasses clink.
Griffin swallows. Tami sips.

Tami.
You know what it is?
I'm a fool…

Griffin.
You're not a fool, Tami…

Tami.
I am…

Griffin.
I'm not going back and forth with you
about this …

Tami.
Then let it lay,
because I'm not folding on it.

Griffin.
You just said you fold all the time.

Tami.
No more.
From this moment on—no more.

Griffin.
Did something else happen today?
The baby clothes should not cause this level of foolishness.

Tami.
I met this young woman earlier today …
While you held up bibs in a boutique,
I watched this young woman try to save someone else's passion.

Griffin.
Is she a student of yours?

Tami.
We rejected her boyfriend's portfolio,
and she came to my office to know the reason.

Griffin.
What'd you tell her?

Tami.
It doesn't matter.
The point is she asked me to look at his work she had on her phone.
And I did. I looked. I gave feedback. Even though I shouldn't have.

Griffin.
And you did because …?

Tami.
I'm a fool.
Just like I'm a fool for trusting you to take
back those clothes.
I should do it.

Griffin.
You don't have my card.
You'd need my debit.

Tami pretends she's in conversation with the sales person at the baby boutique.

Tami.
'Hi. Yes. I want to return these clothes.
My husband decided to splurge
on a baby that will never come to be.
You see, I'm barren and—'

Griffin.
You shouldn't jinx yourself like that—

Tami.
'And he's an optimist.
He says I'm negative, but he's really just gullible.'

Griffin.
Gullible?

Tami.
'So please take these clothes back,
transfer the funds to a gift card,
and I can gift a co-worker who has
an actual bun in the oven.'

Griffin.
Who's pregnant in your department?

Tami.
I'm sure somebody is or will be … there's never
a lack of expecting on campus.

Griffin.
The way things are moving for me,
I may be expecting longer than I anticipated.

Tami.
What do you mean?

Griffin.
I tried to make an appointment with
a lawyer earlier today. But I couldn't do it.

Tami.
Why?

Griffin.
I hate lawyers.
I hate the legal system.
I hate the paperwork, the forms, the files. Even the got-dang
paperclips, the folders.
Three hundred and eighty-two days ago, when I made my first step as
a free man,
I said never again would I get caught up in that system.
And this afternoon I'm on the phone calling a law office.

Tami.
You can't let it be the same system.

Griffin.
Tell that to my gut. My nerves.
After I failed that call, I left here
and ended up at that baby shop.

Tami.
Retail therapy.

Griffin.
Post-traumatic therapy.
=.=
That young woman showing up at your office like that,
it took guts.

Tami.
It did.

Griffin.
Do you think she'll let me borrow some of hers?

Tami.
Griffin …

Griffin.
What she did—that's something you would've done.

Tami.
I know.
And at her age, I would've been standing there
fighting for Stevie.
It took me a minute to figure out she
was not the woman to fight for.

Griffin.
Stevie was crazy.
She was controlling, selfish, and insane.
If I had been free, I would've rung her neck
for hurting you the way she did.

Tami.
You can't use violence to stop violence.

Griffin.
You can use it to protect the people you love.

Tami.
You learned that while serving time?

Griffin.
A lesson I never practiced, but I saw it go down
again and again.

Tami.
=.=
Do you want me to call that lawyer for you?
Make an appointment?

Griffin.
No, no, I have to do that for myself.
=.=
=.=
So … you folded because you saw a bit of yourself in that young
woman.

Tami.
Maybe.

Griffin.
Or maybe … you just saw a lot of yourself wrapped around that
young woman …

Tami.
Griffin …

Griffin.
I'm just hypothesizing …

Tami.
I can help that girl without being attracted to her.

Griffin.
Can you?
Did you?

Tami.
Shut up and fold your baby clothes.

7.

In 2014, Stokes reads another one of G.K.Marche's novels.
In 1966, G.K.Marche types the novel that Stokes reads.

G.K.
=.=[*types*]
=.=[*types*]
[*reads aloud what's just been written*]
"The door clicked shut behind her. Tears gathered. A hushed breeze escorted her away, towards a freedom. "If not achieved by Martin or Malcolm, then who?" she worried. The sun kissed her face, eager to show her the possibilities of tomorrow. Grateful for the love, she began a journey—for her salvation, for her ancestors, for herself."

G.K. sits back relieved.
She removes the sheet of paper from the typewriter,
and places it face down on thick stack of paper.

She puts on a merengue album.
A song fills the space.

G.K. sways to the beat—grateful, exhausted, excited.
She executes a few steps.

Natalie enters, a bit cautious.

Natalie.
You finished *Midnight Song?*

G.K.
On this night, in this year of 1966,
Midnight Song is finished!
Novel number 2, baby!

Excitement, relief from both women.
They dance. Natalie leads.

G.K. and Natalie kiss.

They dance. Kiss. Dance. Kiss.
Forget the dancing—they kiss.
The music plays.
G.K. and Natalie exit towards the bedroom.
The music follows them.

In 2014, Stokes reads the published version of this novel.
The song played in 1966 now echoes somewhere in the distance
in Stokes' neighborhood. He's engrossed.

Riley enters. A bit groggy.

> **Riley.**
> You coming to bed?

> **Stokes.**
> In a bit.

> **Riley.**
> It's late.

> **Stokes.**
> =.=

> **Riley.**
> You made progress since this morning.
> That's still *Midnight Song*, yea?

> **Stokes.**
> Yup.

Awkward moments pass.

> **Riley.**
> You can read in bed, Stokes.

> **Stokes.**
> Let me finish this chapter …

Riley goes to lay down next to Stokes.

> **Stokes.**
> Go back to bed, Riley.
> I'll be there soon.

Riley stops.
A bit rejected.

135

Riley, frustrated, exits.

Stokes continues to read.

8.

Riley returns to Tami's office.

Riley.
He stopped painting.

Tami.
How did you get in?
The same person let you in?

Riley.
A different one.

Tami.
Those guards are useless.

Riley.
They think I'm a student.

Tami.
Why are you back here?

Riley.
He's binge reading a stack of G.K.Marche novels.

Tami.
G.K.Marche...

Riley.
You know her work?

Tami.
Mm-hm. I haven't heard that name in years tho ...
Let the brotha read. She's good. Underrated.

Riley.
He hasn't painted since he got your rejection letter.
All he's been doing is reading her books.

Tami.
With him binge reading and you showing up at my office uninvited,
how do you pay rent?

Riley.
Stokes is a handler at a few galleries.
I work at that computer repair shop on Hayes & Stewart.
The rent is covered.
I'm more worried about his creativity account.
I think he's depressed.
Don't you talk to students who are unhappy?
Who can't paint? Won't paint?

Tami.
Yes, I do.
And those are students who have been accepted
and have enrolled in the program.
Mister Michelle has not been accepted.

Riley.
Do you still paint?

Tami.
Of course ...

Riley.
Don't you get depressed?

Tami.
That's none of your business.

Riley points out a painting on the fourth wall.

Riley.
Is this your work?

Tami.
No.

Riley.
Do you know the person who painted it?

Tami.
Yes.

Riley.
Who is he?

Tami.
She.

Riley.
Who is <u>she</u>?

Tami.
An ex. My ex …

Riley.
She painted this for you?

Tami.
=.=
Yes.

Riley.
And it's hanging in your office.

Tami.
Yes.

Riley.
And do you know why?

Tami.
I'm sensing you have a theory …

Riley.
Because to see that painting is to know
someone created something because of you,
for you. That's a powerful thing.

Tami.
I'm just too lazy to take it down.

Riley.
You keep that painting on your wall;
I carry Stokes's work in my phone.
You and I have tangible reminders of
how we made someone feel …

Tami looks to the painting. She sees a memory that pulls her in, but she quickly looks away. Shakes her head, rejecting that journey. Riley sees this. Tami sees that Riley saw this.

Tami.
Maybe it's a reminder to <u>not</u> feel a certain way again …

Riley.
Either way it's there for a reason…
=.=
=.=
What if it was me?
What if I was the depressed artist?

Tami.
Are you?

Riley.
I could be.
I do graphic design … on the side.
I could be depressed.

Tami.
Have I seen your stuff?

Riley.
I doubt it.

Tami.
Where can I see it?
You have any of <u>your</u> work on your phone?

Riley.
No.

Tami.
You should.

Riley.
So you would help me right now?
If I said to you: "Miss Sterling-Brown, I know
I'm not a student here, but I'm a depressed graphic designer…"

Tami.
First I would say:
call me Tami.
And then …
=.=
=.=
Yes.
Yes, I would help you.

Riley.
You would?

Tami.
I would.

Riley.
And what would you say?

Tami.
To you?

Riley.
To me.

Tami.
I see you, Ms. Riley.

Tami. (continued)
I see who you are. Who you could be.
It's in your eyes. On your skin.
Twisted in your hair.
Embedded in your breath.
You walk a rhythm of possibility.
There's a trace of that possibility in your scent.
The last time you left my office, that trace
stayed in here with me for hours. I left this office early that day.
And this time, I'll leave soon after you.
=.=
You hide your passion in someone else's.
You need help to love your own possibility.

Riley.
I, I don't need any …
I don't know who you think you see but …
=.=
You don't know anything about who I am …
who I need to be …
=.=
=.=

Riley turns to leave.
Riley is gone.

9.

Griffin tries to make the call again. This time he holds a small teddy bear as he dials. It serves as a security blanket / mascot as he makes the call.

The phone rings from his end.

Receptionist.
Good afternoon, Newton and Bayles Law Office.
How may I help you?

Griffin.
Hello … I.

Griffin panics.
He ends the call. Exhales in frustration. Looks to the teddy bear.

Griffin. [*pep talk mode*]
It's alright.
I'll get it together.
I will.
=.=
I have to.

10.

The park.

1966, G.K. and Natalie sit on a bench to have lunch.
2014, Stokes sits nearby reading one of G.K's books. A half-eaten sandwich rests in his lap.
Occasionally, he swats the air shooing a fly from his food. For the most part he remains engrossed in the book.

The women are playful and carefree.

G.K.
And what is on the menu today?

Natalie.
This lunch will feature our popular "pay day" selection.
Items on the menu consist of delicacies available to us
when money has come in.
[*presents the items*]
Turkey melts from Cooper's …

G.K.
Ooo, I love the turkey melt from Cooper's …

Natalie.
Two slightly cool bottles of Coke.
They were cold when I bought them.

G.K.
That's ok, baby …
And for dessert, I present …
[*reveals a misshapen bit of food wrapped in plastic*]
Oh no …

Natalie.
What is that?

G.K.
It used to be a slice of blueberry pie from Gordon's bakery.
But now …

Natalie.
But now it's…

G.K.
Well, it still is.

Natalie.
It's just smushed.
I'm sure it's still delicious.

G.K.
It must've happened when I fell …

Natalie.
You fell?

G.K.
I didn't want to be late.

Natalie.
What happened?

G.K.
Running for the trolley. My feet stopped listening
to my brain. And plop.
But I got up, and I made it.

Natalie.
You did.

G.K.
The price paid is a smushed pie.

Natalie.
Less chewing for us.
You didn't hurt yourself, did you?

G.K.
My embarrassment is a little tender,
but seeing this [*re: Natalie's*] face is the best medicine there is.

Natalie smiles, blushes.

G.K.
My lil' fall did help me lock in the idea for the next book.

Natalie.
Oh, that's nice.
What is it?

G.K.
You know I want to write
about the riot that broke out over in North Hill …

Natalie.
After that young cop …

G.K.
Killed that kid, yea.
My book will start with a peaceful protest
of a similar event. Then that protest is provoked to violence.

Natalie.
And the fall …?

G.K.
Well during the riot
a woman who was there to protest
is now trying to escape.
She <u>falls</u>, but a stranger catches her.
She looks up, sees the man, and instantly
recognizes the face.

Natalie.
Who is it?

G.K.
Well, that part I don't know yet.
But I know it'll be mysterious.
Someone who she believed had disappeared,
but now the person is back, and she lands in his arms.

Natalie.
Maybe the title could be: *The Fall* by G.K. Marche.

G.K.
I'll start work on it tonight.
The publisher will eat it up.

Natalie.
Tonight?

G.K.
Yea.

Natalie.
Don't you want to relax a bit?
You just spent all that time on the last one.

G.K.
I can't sit on an idea when it strikes.
You know that, Nat.

Natalie.
I know but …
I thought maybe you and I could …
=.=
I have some exciting news to share.

G.K.
Yea? What's that?

Natalie.

A girl from the shop showed some ties I designed to her uncle and he flipped for them.

He placed an order, Gina. My very first order!

G.K.

That's fantastic!

Natalie.

I'm really jazzed about it.

G.K.

You should be.

Natalie.

He and I ended up chatting on the phone.

And it was a lovely conversation.

He's the headmaster at a boarding school in Macino.

And he invited me up to meet the students.

I'll be a guest speaker for the girls in Home Ec!

G.K.

[*genuine*]

That's great! That's really fantastic!

Why am I just hearing about all this?

Natalie.

You were working on your book.

G.K.

Well you could've mentioned it …

Natalie.

You're not the kindest kitten

in the cage when you're …

G.K.

When do you go?

Natalie.

Tomorrow.

G.K.
Tomorrow?

Natalie.
Yes, and I want you to come with me.
We could stay overnight, make a mini-vacation out of it.

G.K.
How would we get there?

Natalie.
Thom will let me borrow his car.

G.K.
Thom?

Natalie.
He manages the wholesale store the shop buys from.
You met him at that summer party my boss hosted.

G.K.
[*remembering*]
Oh yea … Thom.
[*mimics him*]
"Yea, yea … all I read is Black writers: Richard, Ralph, W.E.B, Leroi …
you know those cats?"
[*breaks it*]
It's 1966, he can't name one sista?

Natalie.
Nobody can read everybody, Gina …

G.K.
[*continues*]
"My wife probably knows your work. She's always reading women
books."

Natalie.
He's a nice man.

G.K.
Nice enough to lend you his car.

Natalie.
Come with me.
I don't want to make the drive by myself.

G.K.
But this new book, Nat ...

Natalie.
You can work in the car, during the ride.

G.K.
I can only write at my desk.

Natalie.
Why does it feel like I'm begging you to do this?
I shouldn't have to beg you to—

G.K.
You know how hard it's been ...
I hadn't written a single word
in <u>so</u> many years.

Natalie.
=.= *[remembering]*
I know ...

G.K.
And suddenly words are pouring
from my fingers, Natalie.

In 2014, Stokes reads.
Griffin enters. He sits. He reads the manuscript Tami gifted him earlier.

Natalie.
=.=
It's fine, Gina.
=.=
You should stay and work on the next book.

Natalie. (continued)
=.=
Maybe one of the girls from the shop
can ride up with me.

G.K.
You'll be great.
I know it.
And I want to hear all about it
afterwards, ok?

G.K. kisses Natalie on the cheek who accepts the gesture, but something has shifted between the two women.

The women eat.
The men read.
The sounds of the park swell in the distance.

Natalie.
I, I should head back to the shop …

G.K.
I'll walk you.

In 2014, Griffin asks Stokes:

Griffin.
Excuse me, do you have a pencil?

Stokes.
No, I'm sorry.

Griffin.
My pen dried up.
I need to make a note in the margins here.

Stokes.
Write a note in your phone.

Griffin.
What's that?

Stokes.
I just take notes in my phone.
I don't carry pens, pencils, or any of that anymore.
It's all in my phone.

Griffin.
Oh. Oh right.
I'm … I'm still getting used to having one of these.

Griffin retrieves his phone.
He pecks away for a moment.

The men fall silent, return to reading.

Stokes glances over at Griffin's reading material.

Stokes.
Are you in publishing?

Griffin.
Me? No.

Stokes.
Oh.

Griffin.
Why do you ask?

Stokes.
That sticker on the cover of your book
says: advance review copy.

Griffin.
This? Oh yes.
But no—I'm not in publishing.

Stokes.
Oh.

Griffin.
Are you a writer?

Stokes.
Am I a writer …?
=.= [*considers it*]
Yes.

Griffin.
Really?
What do you write?

Stokes.
Fiction. Prose.

Griffin.
Are you published anywhere?

Stokes.
Not yet. No.
I'm mostly just a reader these days.

Griffin.
Readers are important.

Stokes.
Yea …

Griffin.
Who are you reading?

Stokes.
G.K.Marche.

Griffin.
She's a good writer.

Stokes.
I know, right?

Griffin.
People don't appreciate her like they should.

Stokes.
What have you read?

Griffin.
Everything.

Stokes.
Everything?

Griffin.
Thirty-five novels, four collections of short stories,
two essay collections, one book of poetry.
Everything. There was a time in my life
when I had nothing but time.
How did you find her?

Stokes.
By chance.
I got my hands on twenty books.

Griffin.
No way…

Stokes.
Yes! And I planned to sell them—
I figured a local writer might fetch a solid price,
but then I read a few pages of one book, and now
I'm six novels deep and I can't stop.

Griffin.
Same thing happened to me.
I had a friend who hooked me up with her books.
And I read page after page, volume after volume.
G.K. used to live in the Tenderloin.

Stokes.
I read that on her Wikipedia page.

Griffin.
When my kid hits 16, G.K.Marche will definitely be required reading.

Stokes.
How old is he now?

Griffin.
Oh … well, I'm expecting.

Stokes.
Congratulations.

Griffin.
Thank you.

Stokes.
Boy or girl?

Griffin.
Don't know.
As long as it's healthy.

Stokes.
I hear that.
You're gonna be a cool dad.
Letting your kid read G.K.Marche
at 16.

Griffin.
She's an important part of Black women's literature;
women's literature in general; Black queer literature specifically.
Just American literature as a whole.

Stokes.
Yea but …

Griffin.
You don't think so?

Stokes.

I do … it's just …
I'm in my late 20s and some of the stuff
she writes about makes <u>me</u> uncomfortable.

Griffin.

Have you read much literature by Black women?

Stokes.

No.

Griffin.

That's why you're uncomfortable.
But it's good that you're still reading
in spite of your discomfort.

Stokes.

You sound like a professor.

Griffin.

I'm not.

Stokes.

Did you study Black literature in college?

Griffin.

I didn't go to college.
I just read a bunch of books.

Stokes.

The spare time.

Griffin.

Not spare—more like sentenced.
I was locked up.

Stokes.

For how long?

Griffin.
Twenty-five years.

Stokes.
Damn … what'd you do?

Griffin.
That's just it.
I didn't do the crime they charged me with.

Stokes.
Are you pulling my leg?

Griffin.
I am not.
I spent 25 years of a 75-year sentence
for a crime I did not commit.

Stokes.
Shit.

Griffin.
So I had the time to read.

Stokes.
I'm sure you did.

Griffin.
My mother gave me my first G.K. book.
But her and my friend sent me a bunch of writers
before that: Angela Davis, bell hooks, Alice Walker, Audre Lorde,
Jewelle Gomez, Cheryl Clarke, Sista Souljha, Adrienne Kennedy …
So while I did not attend college, those women did take me to school.
=.=
How old are you?

Stokes.
Twenty-eight.

Griffin.
I was your age when I started reading G.K.
By the time I started her body of work,
I had already read a ton of other women.
So I wasn't uncomfortable.
My kid won't be either. Sixteen will be a good age to read G.K.

Stokes.
You only read Black women?

Griffin.
No. But I studied the many lessons they taught.
While other brothas serving time transformed into Black Muslims,
I became a Black feminist.

Stokes.
For real?

Griffin.
Yes.

Stokes.
What does that even mean?

Griffin.
It means our collective liberation
can be achieved when we eradicate
oppression against Black women.

Stokes.
I've, I've heard of brothas like you … but …

Griffin.
Never seen one in real life?

Stokes.
Right.
And they're usually … younger.
Wrapped up in a post-everything mentality.

Griffin.
I'm just post-ignorance.

Stokes.
Is that book about Black women?

Griffin.
This? This is a book about slums written
by a 60 year-old white, balding
sociologist. The friend who sent me books while I was
incarcerated, gave me this one. She knew I was excited for it to come
out.

Stokes.
That's a good friend.

Griffin.
She's a great friend.
We had just gotten to know each other
right before I got caught up in the legal system.
She was a young painter.
I was a young thinker, small time dealer.

Stokes.
What did they lock you up for?

Griffin.
It doesn't matter because I didn't do it.

Stokes.
Ok.

Griffin.
Keep reading G.K.
She's good for you.
Which book are you reading now?

Stokes and Griffin continue their conversation as ...

11.

Riley's job.

Riley.
What are you doing here?

Tami.
My hard drive crashed.

Riley.
You're crazy.

Tami.
I'm a customer.

Riley.
It just crashed?

Tami.
Not too long ago.

Riley.
And you brought it here?

Tami.
Yes. I want to see if I can save anything.

Riley.
They have IT on your campus.

Tami.
The wait is too long.

Riley.
How do you know what the wait is here?

Tami.
I don't. That's why I'm here.
To find that out.
How long will it take for you to fix this?

Riley.
I'll find someone to do a diagnostic.

Tami.
You can't do it?

Riley.
I can do it.
But I don't want to.

Tami.
Don't you get a commission
for every case you close?

Riley.
This isn't a detective agency.
It's tech repair.
We don't work on commission. It's not a chain store.
We're paid decent wages because we have a valuable skill.

Tami.
Sorry.

Riley.
Are you just saying that because
you want your laptop fixed?

Tami.
Of course I am.

Riley.
I'll find somebody else to help you—

Tami.
But I also mean it:
I'm sorry.

Riley.
=.=

Tami.
And I also want to apologize for what I said to you
the last time you were in my office.
I was out of line.

Riley.
You were.

Tami.
It'd be great if *you* could find out what can be saved
on my laptop.

Riley deliberates. She eventually opens the laptop. Powers it up.

Tami.
Thank you.

Riley.
I'm only doing this so I can laugh
at your stupid files being destroyed.

Tami.
That's fine.
That's okay.
As long as you can –

Riley laughs. And laughs. And laughs.
Tami takes it, patiently waits.
Riley's laugh subsides.

Tami.
No files?

Riley.
The skull & bones gif is a solid indication.
You picked up a virus.

Tami.
Great.

Riley.
Is this a personal computer,
or does it belong to the school?

Tami.
Personal.

Riley.
If our store opens this device
to repair it, it could void your warranty.

Tami.
I don't care …

Riley.
It's store policy to tell you that.

Tami.
Is it store policy to laugh in my face?

Riley.
No, that's my policy when karma
works its magic.

12.

*1966 G.K. sits in her apartment. She sketches out a new novel, pen and pad engaged.
In 2014:*

Stokes.
[*excited.*]
Hey.

Riley.
Hi.

Stokes.
How was your day?

Riley.
Good.
You seem like yours was better than good.

Stokes.
It was. It is.
Great. Guess what?

Riley.
You got an acceptance letter?!

Stokes.
What? No. No no.
=.=
I want to write a novel.

Riley.
=.=

Stokes.
Did you hear me?

Riley.
A novel?

Stokes.
Yes.

Riley.
Ok …

Stokes.
That's really exciting!
It's a big deal …

Riley.
When did you decide this?

Stokes.
I met this guy today in the park—

Riley.
You didn't go to work today?

Stokes.
I did. I went to the gallery.
I met him during my lunch break.
Baby … be happy for me.
Can't you see how excited I am about this?

Riley.
What am I supposed to say?

Stokes.
Ask me what I want to write about?

Riley.
What do you want to write about?

Stokes.
A guy whose girl is being so lame right now.

Riley.
Stokes, that isn't fair.

Stokes.
I'm not being fair?

Riley.
What about your painting?
You haven't touched your brushes in almost a—

Stokes.
And you're the <u>only</u> <u>person</u> who cares.

Riley.
But <u>nobody</u> cares if you write a novel.

Stokes.
Griffin cares!

Riley.
Who is Griffin??!

Stokes.
He's a member of the post-ignorance literati.

Riley.
That's some whack Tumblr lingo.
Do you want pizza for dinner?

Stokes.
I don't want any of that shit.

Riley.
Stokes, what is going on with you?
Talk to me. I want to help you fix this.

Stokes.
Who says anything is broken?

Riley.
I do. I say it is.

Stokes grabs his coat and laptop.

Riley.
Now you're leaving?

Stokes.
I need some air.

Riley.
Stokes, if you would just <u>let go</u>
and stop trying to control
the canvas, you would depict a stronger
perspective with your painting.

Stokes stops.

Stokes.
=.=
What? Where did that come from?

Riley.
You shouldn't turn your back
on your art.

Stokes.
People paint with words all the time.

G.K. loads her typewriter.

Riley.
That's not you.

G.K. pecks away at the keys—the beginning of a new novel.

Stokes.
=.=

Riley.
=.=

Stokes.
=.=

Stokes leaves.

Riley is left alone, empty.
G.K. writes alone.

13.

Griffin's apartment.

Griffin.
You went to homegurl's job?

Tami.
My computer died.

Griffin.
You have IT on campus.

Tami.
Shut up.

Griffin.
Tami … you are too old for that shit.
Maybe if you were in your early 30s.
But not now. Don't do this now.

Tami.
My Com.Pu.Ter Died, Griffin.

Griffin.
U.Ain't.Fool.In.No.Body.In.Here.
You come into my home, and try to feed me a slice
a bullshit pie?

Tami.
Can I have another glass of wine?

Griffin.
You need it.
Drown your shame in some Malbec.
=.=
You are interested in her.

Tami.
She's too young.
=.=
Do you want more wine?

Griffin.
Tami…

Tami.
She has a boyfriend, Griffin.

Griffin.
We are a master at being evasive this evening.

Tami.
She has a boyfriend.

Griffin.
Do you like her? Yes or no—

Tami.
A boyfriend who was rejected from my program.
It's too … complicated.
I'm too … complicated.

Tami. (continued)
I'm getting wine. I also have to pee.

Griffin.
Drown that shame, girl!

Tami exits.

The doorbell rings.

Griffin answers it.

Stokes.
Hi.

Griffin.
Stokes.

Stokes.
Can I …? I'm sorry.
Is this a bad thing that I'm here?

Griffin.
Uhhh…

Stokes.
You told me you lived in the new high rise
right off Market,
and I saw your name on the intercom directory downstairs.
Is this weird?

Griffin.
No no no. Yes. Yes it is weird.

Stokes.
I'm sorry.

Griffin.
How did you get past the…?

Stokes.

Your doorman and I painted houses together last summer.

I just … I was so inspired by our conversation this afternoon.

I went home to talk to my girl about it,

and she wasn't … I mean, when I really think about it

I expected that behavior from her.

I did. I expected it.

Can I come in?

Tami.

[*offstage*]

Griffin, you bought a fucking crib?!?

Tami enters with a full glass of wine.
She sees Stokes. Stokes sees her.

Stokes.

Oh. Oh, you are busy.

Tami.

Hello.

Griffin.

Stokes this is Tami…

Stokes.

Hi …

I can go.

Sorry to –

Tami.

No way.

You should come in.

Come in. Griffin and I were just chatting.

Griffin steps to the side.
Stokes enters.

Stokes.

Whoa …this is a nice apartment.

Griffin.
Thank you.

Tami.
It is fabulous, right?

Griffin.
[*to Stokes*] Do you want a glass of wine?

Stokes.
I'll have a beer if you got any.
How long have you lived here?

As Griffin exits to get Stokes a beer:

Griffin.
A little over a year.

Tami.
Griffin was one of the first tenants to move in the building.
I helped him decorate.

Griffin.
[*off*] It took a minute to get used to all this space.

Tami.
[*yells to Griffin*] Did you tell him about your studies abroad?

Stokes.
He studied abroad?

As Griffin enters with Stokes' beer.

Griffin.
Yes, I told him I served time.

Stokes.
Oh. Yea, he did.

Griffin.
My first three months living here, I slept on the pantry floor.

Griffin. (continued)

After ninety-two hundred days living in a 6x10 cage
with cinderblock walls, it was hard to be okay with having this much space.

My own space.

Stokes.

Why not get a smaller apartment?

Tami.

[*smiling*] Yea, Griffin, why not?

Griffin.

You know why not, Tami.

[*to Stokes*] There's a whole story about it.

She loves this story.

Tami.

I do. I do love this story.

Griffin.

Well why don't you tell it, since you love it—

Tami.

Before Griffin got caught up in the legal system,
he used to run all up and through this neighborhood.
This was way before the fancy shops and hibachi restaurants.

Griffin.

I was rolling with a tough group of dudes...

Tami.

There was a time in his life when Griffin slept in a shelter.

Griffin.

I was young and angry. Having a hard time at home.

Tami.

And that shelter used to be right where this high rise now sits.
Fast forward to last year: Griffin's case gets overturned.

Tami. (continued)
It becomes a huge media story because Griffin is so interesting and charming.
He talks about Black feminism. He quotes Woody Guthrie—who <u>is</u> this Black man?
With every newspaper and tv interview he becomes a bit of a media darling.

Griffin.
I'm not anybody's <u>darling</u>—

Tami.
You are. Get over it.
So the man who now owns this land is so impressed by Griffin and angered
by our broken legal system, he gifts him this apartment.
Can you believe that? I still can't believe it.
But it's a story I fucking love.

Griffin.
Please forgive my friend, Stokes.
That Malbec she's sipping on is making
her story-telling even more hype than it usually is.

Tami.
I'm fine. I'm fine …
Don't be silly, Griffin.
Stokes … Stokes … it's so funny.
You're the second person I've dealt with that has that name.

Stokes.
Really? That is funny. I've never met another Stokes.

Griffin.
Is it a family name?

Stokes.
My great-grandfather.

Tami.

And how do you know Griffin?

Did you hear him give his "I am a Black feminist" lecture?

Stokes.

No … no. Actually we met earlier today.

Tami.

Really?

Griffin.

He commented on the book you recently gifted me.

The advance copy.

Tami.

Oh yes.

Stokes.

And he commented on the fact

that I was reading G.K.Marche.

Tami takes a pause.

Griffin.

Stokes is a writer.

Stokes.

Aspiring.

Tami.

Oh … that's nice.

What are you working on now?

Stokes.

Well, I have my eye set on completing my first novel.

Griffin.

Do you know what it'll be about?

Stokes.
Well I have general thoughts, but nothing concrete yet.
My girlfriend and I just got into a fight about it.
She's not so supportive about the whole thing.

Tami's phone rings.

Tami.
[*to the* boys]
Excuse me.

Tami answers her phone.

Tami.
Hello?

Riley.
It's Riley.

Tami.
Oh. Oh hi.
How did you get my—

Riley.
I got your number from the form
you filled out earlier today.

Tami.
Ok …

Riley.
Are you busy? Is it okay I'm calling you like this?
This is weird, isn't it?

Tami.
No. No. What's up?

Riley.
Stokes told me he wants to write a novel.

Tami.
=.=

Riley.
He's been reading these shitty G.K.Marche books,
and now he wants to write a novel.

Tami looks over at Stokes.
The pieces are all in place.
Tami = facepalm

Riley.
He stormed out.
I'm here angry and anxious,
and my first thought—let me call Tami.

Tami.
=.=

Riley.
Hello?

Tami.
Hi.

Riley.
Did you hear me?

Tami.
I did.

Riley.
You wanna grab a drink somewhere?
I don't want to be here when he comes back.
I can't.
Are you busy?
I only know tech guys, and I can't talk to tech guys
about boyfriend problems.

Tami.
Drinks? Sure.

Riley.
There's a spot in The Lower Hay I like …

Riley's end of the conversation fades to darkness.
We watch Tami wrap up the conversation.

    Tami.
Uh-huh …
=.=
=.=
Ok.
=.=
=.=
I'll see you there soon.

Tami ends the call.
She turns to the boys.

    Griffin.
Is everything okay?

    Tami.
Yea … I have to go.

    Griffin.
Tami …?

    Tami.
Everything is … fine.
I just have an appointment.
I forgot about.

    Griffin.
Do you want me to fetch you a Lyft?

    Tami.
I got it. I got it.
I'm just going to head downstairs.
Stokes it was … nice meeting you.

Stokes.
Same.

Tami.
Bye.

Tami exits.

14.

In 1966, Natalie comes home late.
Later than G.K. expected.

G.K.
You're back! Finally.
How did it go?
Wait, let me finish this …
[*types*] … sentence.
[*types*] … This thought …
[*types*] ….
[*types*] ……

Natalie.
We can talk about it in the morning…

G.K.
No, I'm done.
I'm done.
Tell me all about it.

Natalie.
It was great.
The students were lovely.
They were so sweet.
I forgot how much I enjoy being around kids.
The class went well.
I delivered the ties, no problem.

G.K.
That's wonderful!

G.K. kisses Natalie.

G.K.
[*tastes the trace of something on Nat's lips*]
Port?

Natalie.
Yes, I had a glass of port after dinner.

G.K.
You already had dinner.

Natalie.
Yes. I figured you would be writing,
and Thom was free.

G.K.
Thom?

Natalie.
He ended up coming with me.
It's his car, and he was free.
So he offered to come up with me.

G.K.
Oh ... well, how about I open a bottle of white
and we unwind? I want to hear everything about today.

Natalie.
Babe, I'm awfully tired.
[*yawns*]
I think I'll just call it a night.
You keep working on your book.
How's it going?

G.K.
It's coming along.

Natalie.
Good. I'm happy for you.
'Night babe.

A peck on the cheek from Natalie.
She exits.

G.K. is left with her typewriter.

15.

Riley.
Most of G.K.'s books are out of print.
His desire to write is sparked by an out of print author.
Ain't that some shit?
I'm having another ginger whiskey.
You want another vodka soda?

Tami.
I'm fine.

Riley.
He's been painting since junior high.
And now all of a sudden …

Tami.
Let him write some fiction.
Why not?

Riley.
Because it's a reaction to rejection.

Tami.
As opposed to?

Riley.
A choice of artistic expression.
He's dropping his brushes because of rejection.

Tami.
Constant rejection is hard!

Riley.
It's life.
I love computers, right?

Riley. (continued)
Ever since I was a kid.
Do you realize how many douches there are in tech?
Socially awkward white boys, dismissive Asian guys,
and there's always the lone white woman who's afraid to talk to me
because
she doesn't want to appear weak in front of the other guys?
That shit is hard.
<u>And</u> I'm Black.
<u>And</u> I'm from a small mid-western town.
<u>And</u> I didn't grow up with a lot of money.
<u>And</u> my aunt was the only person in my family who encouraged me.
Nothing in my pedigree suggests I would be accepted into tech society.

Tami.
Did you just say "pedigree"…?

Riley.
I've been rejected a million times.
More than a million.
But I said: fuck you, nut stain, I have every right to be here.
I can code. I can reroute an x23c fucking blindfolded—

Tami.
What's an x—

Riley.
It's a complicated network system.
I can analyze algorithms with my ass.
I deserve to be in the room, in the program.
I earned my degree.
And those guys respected me in the end.
He has to use rejection as motivation, not confirmation.

Tami.
How are you this rigid?
People your age are supposed to wander.

Riley.
I do! I wander!

Tami.
When? How?

Riley.
With Stokes—

Tami.
Can I ask a favor?

Riley.
What?

Tami.
No more Stokes bashing.

Riley.
Excuse me?

Tami.
Can you not rag on the brotha
for a second? He seems like sweet guy.
[*Catching herself*] From his application.
I remember his artistic statement.
He seemed sweet.

Riley.
I'm not ragging on—

Tami.
Yes, you are.

Riley.
No, I'm—

Tami.
Yea, you—

Riley.
Can I finish a sent—

Tami.
Only if you recognize and stop the ragging.

Riley.	**Tami.**
I—	Ah.
Stop—	Nope.
=.=	=.=
=.=	=.=
Gah—	Shttt.
=.=	=.=
=.=	=.=
Alright!	Ah!
Okay! Alright!	

The playfulness of the exchange may cause a smile or light laughter between the women.

Riley.
I want to tell you something.

Tami.
What?

Riley.
I like your work.

Tami.
My work?

Riley.
Your paintings.
I found pictures online.

Tami.
Oh. Thank you.

Riley.
Your hands are very … clean.

Tami.
Why wouldn't they be?

Riley.

You don't use brushes, right? You only use your hands to paint.

Tami.

Some times, but I use other things, too.

Riley.

Like what?

Tami.

Well, it depends on the piece.

Riley takes out her phone and pecks on the screen a few times.

Riley.

What about this one?

Tami.

You pulled that up pretty quick—

Riley.

What did you use to make … what's the name of it?

Tami.

Temporário: Interminável …

Riley.

Temporary: Endless … ?

Tami.

Você fala Portuguese?

Riley.

Just enough to daydream about living in Brazil.

Tami.

I lived there for six months and painted a series of pieces—this one included.
You see what can happen when you let yourself wander?

Riley.

I should move to Brasilia?

Tami.
Maybe. You could work on graphic design.

Riley.
Uh-uh. In that heat, I'd make music.

Tami.
You play an instrument?

Riley.
I used to make beats.

Tami.
Beats?

Riley.
You know … [*drums a boom-bap type beat on the table*]

Tami.
Oh … why'd you stop?

Riley.
I just stopped. No real reason.

Tami.
Maybe you should start again.

Riley.
Maybe … so you made "Temporário / Interminável" with your hands and …
what else?

Tami.
Oh. Painting knives. That's how I get the texture.
You can see if you zoom in.

Tami leans closer, uses her fingers to zoom in on Riley's screen.

Tami.
See?

Tami. (continued)
I use a number 41 here … [*uses her fingers to show a different section*] a
number 8, [*a different section*] and 26 here. My hands smooth out bright
hues here …

Riley.
=.=
=.=
I want to tell you something else.

Tami.
What's that?

Riley kisses Tami. They kiss.
Tami breaks away.

Riley.
=.=

Tami.
=.=

Riley.
I'm sorr—

Tami grabs Riley and kisses her.
Riley breaks away.

Riley.
=.=

Tami.
=.=

Riley.
=.=

Tami.
Maybe I should go.

Riley.
Stay.
I just …
I just need a moment to catch my breath.

The women remain unsure what will happen next.
Riley takes Tami's hand.

They sit quietly. They hold hands and sip their respective drinks.

16.

At Griffin's apartment.

Stokes.
My girl and I,
when we first started hanging out
it was so good. So easy.
We had just gotten out of relationships:
She just got dumped by this girl who was a CPA at a big firm.
And I had just gotten dumped by a dancer.
Riley had never dated an artist.
And I had never dated anybody in tech.
But we vibed, you know?

Griffin.
A good vibe is a special thing.

Stokes.
It is.

Griffin.
You want more?

Stokes.
Sure.

Griffin pours Stokes a bit more whiskey.

Stokes.
Are you drunk at all?

Griffin.
Not really.
But you are.

Stokes.
I am. Just a bit though.
=.=
Thank you for letting me sit here with you.
=.=
Sometimes it's easier to sit with a stranger
than with a friend.

Griffin.
I get that.

Stokes.
Not to say you aren't a friend.
But we just met.
I guess you're a buddy, right now.
Or a cool dude.

Griffin.
Becoming a friend takes time.

Stokes.
It does.
=.=
When I first arrived I thought Tami was the mother.

Griffin.
The mother?

Stokes.
You're expecting a baby, right?
I thought Tami was the mother.

Griffin.
Oh. She isn't.

Stokes.
I figured she couldn't be
because she had that big glass of wine.

Griffin.
Well, that's not the only reason she couldn't be,
but yes that might be a deal-breaker for me.

Stokes.
So who is the mother?

Griffin.
I don't know, yet.

Stokes.
You trying to adopt?

Griffin.
I'm preparing. I'm expecting.
I haven't figured out the path to creation yet.

Stokes.
You're a weird dude, Griffin.

Griffin.
I am?

Stokes.
Yea.

Griffin.
So are you.

Stokes.
I guess it's a good thing we found each other.
=.=
Do you know who you want to make a kid with?

Griffin.
No.
I just want her to be a good person from good people.
Smart. Compassionate. Healthy.

Stokes.
You looking for a wife?

Griffin.
When I was younger.
But now I just want to be a father.

Stokes.
You'll do it by yourself?

Griffin.
Yes.

Stokes.
That's a big decision.
=.=
=.=
I couldn't do it.

Griffin.
No?
=.=[*shrugs*]
It's not for everybody.

Stokes.
[*a realization*]
I've never made big life decisions on my own.
I've always had a woman with me.
My mother, all while I was a kid.
Then I've had one girlfriend after the other ever since junior high.
I can't choose anything major without hearing my woman speak on it.

Griffin.
=.=

Stokes.
That's pathetic, right?

Griffin.
It's not pathetic.

Stokes.
=.=
=.=
I'm gonna write a novel.
=.=
=.=
Riley can have an opinion on it,
but it won't change mine.

Griffin.
You should do what makes you happy, Stokes.
What leaves you fulfilled.

Stokes.
Kids are expensive.

Griffin.
They are.

Stokes.
You should adopt.

Griffin.
My … background makes me a less than ideal candidate.

Stokes.
But the conviction was overturned, right?

Griffin.
I have to work with a lawyer to see what can lean in my favor.

Stokes.
That must be weird …

Griffin.
What's that?

Stokes.
To build your legacy, you have to use the same system that tried to stifle you.

Griffin is pleasantly surprised that Stokes sees things this way.

Griffin.
Yes. It is. That is exactly my issue with it.
That fact is kicking me in my gut right now.

Stokes.
A kid is a part of your legacy.

Griffin.
And to have the system caught up in this really personal journey is … it's … tough.

Stokes.
You have to see the system as a tool, not the overseer.

Griffin.
Easier tried than achieved.

Stokes.
What about surrogacy?
That can be between just you and the woman, right?

Griffin.
No, I need two different women for that.
One to donate the egg and one to carry the child.

Stokes.
And it's expensive, too … right?

Griffin.
Very.
But I'm keeping all options open at this point.

Stokes.
=.=

Griffin.
=.=

Stokes.
Creation is hard work.

Griffin.
It is.

Stokes.
If I find women who might be a good fit,
should I …?

Griffin.
You focus on your writing, Stokes.
Create your own masterpiece, and I'll manage
creating mine.

17.

Griffin is on the phone again. This time he holds a piece of paper.

The phone rings from his end.

Receptionist.
Good afternoon, Newton and Bayles—

Griffin dives right into reading his written statement:

Griffin.
Good afternoon. My name is Griffin B. Charles.
I am a single Black American man, 47 years-old,
and I want to be a father. I recognize this is a need
and desire that I carry deeply in my heart.
I understand fatherhood is not
a right. I recognize my relationship with the legal system
may prevent my access to any guarantees, but it is within
my right to pursue the fact that I want to be a father.

Griffin. (continued)
I am not ashamed of my life. I have nothing to hide.
I stand in the truth of my past, so that I can create the light
of my future. In this journey that I'm just now beginning I already
sometimes feel helpless, but I want to claim my power to spend my
time, my effort, and my currency to make this desire, this need a
reality.
That is why I am calling your office this morning. I want a consultation
with Mrs. Newton to discuss
her legal services for independent adoption as well as surrogacy.

Griffin finishes his speech slightly winded.
He stands frozen unsure of the consequence. Suddenly, he hears hold music playing, Rod
Stewart's "Forever Young", or something just as lite rock-ish.

Griffin.
Hello?

Suddenly:

Receptionist.
Good afternoon, Newton and Bayles Law Offices.
Thank you for holding. How can I help you?

Griffin exhales. The tension of the moment completely deflated. But he manages to say:

Griffin.
I want to talk to a lawyer about adoption
and surrogacy.

18.

Riley powers on her beat machine.
Tami stands at her easel, paint knife in hand.
She watches Riley, eager to see what will happen.

Riley.
This is a song about creation.

Riley presses buttons on the beat machine.
She builds a beat from scratch right before our eyes/ears.

The beat blossoms. Tami rocks to the beat.

In 1966, G.K.Marche works on rewrites of her latest novel. It doesn't look as if it's going well.

In 2014, Stokes writes on his laptop. It looks as if it's going okay (!)

In 1966, Natalie works at the shop after hours. She sits at her sewing machine. A man reaches from the shadows and strokes her hair. Natalie takes the hand and gently kisses it.

Riley builds a remix of the mix she just created. Tami cheers.

In 2014, Griffin continues his conversation with a lawyer. We can't hear the conversation, but Griffin looks concerned more than hopeful.

In 1966, G.K.Marche checks the clock. Natalie should've been home by now.

In 2014, Stokes creates word after word, image after image.

Griffin pleads his case.

Tami paints on the canvas in between dance moves.

In 1966, Natalie is wrapped around a man—this is Thom. She is in the throes of creation with this man named Thom. Intimate, raw, passionate, necessary, inevitable consummation occurs.

In 2014, Riley almost seems to orchestrate the simultaneous activity on stage.

Emotions/sensations/rhythms/sounds reach a collective …
climax.

Stillness.

End of Act One

19.

Split scene.
In 1966 / 2014:

Natalie.	**Riley.**
I'm pregnant.	I'm pregnant.
G.K.	**Stokes.**
=.=	=.=
Natalie.	**Riley.**
=.=	=.=
G.K.	**Stokes.**
=.=	=.=
Natalie.	**Riley.**
Did you hear me?	Did you hear me?
G.K.	**Stokes.**
I did.	I did.
How … ?	How … ?

Natalie.
A moment of weakness …

Riley.
… in the bedroom … we had
a fight in the evening
but then you came to me in
the night …

G.K.
With who?

Stokes.
What about your pill?

Natalie.
It doesn't matter.

Riley.
Obviously it didn't work.

G.K.
It matters to me.
Fuck, Natalie …

Stokes.
Fuck, Riley …

Natalie.
I want to raise it with you.

G.K.
=.=

Riley.
=.=

Natalie.
We can keep it.

Stokes.
Are you sure?

Riley.
Yes, I'm sure.

Natalie.
I want this baby to be ours.

G.K.
What about the father?

Natalie.
He doesn't matter anymore.

Stokes.
What are we gonna do?

G.K.
Does he know that?

Riley.
I don't know … we're not
okay … this baby

Riley. (continued)
isn't the thing we need …

Natalie.
I don't care what he knows
or doesn't know.

Stokes.
=.= [*goes to Riley.*]

Riley.
=.= [*steps back.*]

Natalie.
I want us to raise something
together.

Stokes.
Riley … [*takes another step*]

Riley.
=.= [*lets Stokes come closer.*]

Stokes embraces Riley.

Natalie.
You write novels.
I work at the shop.
We lead separate lives, but
we can raise this together.

Stokes holds Riley.

She clings to him.

G.K.
We just ignore how it got here?

Natalie.
We can create a new journey.
A new story grows inside me.

Natalie. (continued)
You and I can claim this child.
It won't know any other way, but us.

G.K.
Nat, we have to pick and choose
where it's okay to hold hands,
whisper I love you.
How can you and I raise a child
in a space of negotiation?

                                          Stokes.
                                          Let's keep it.

20.

Tami's apartment.

Tami.
=.=

Riley.
=.=

Tami.
=.=

Riley.
=.=

Tami.
What are you gonna do?

Riley.
I don't know.

Tami.
What did Stokes say?

Riley.
He wants to keep it.

Tami.
He does?

Riley.
He wants us to raise it.

Tami.
Shit …

Riley.
I know …

Tami.
How do you feel about that?

Riley.
I'm still reeling from the idea
that there's … a thing growing inside of me.
=.=
I got wasted not too long ago.

Tami.
I know. I was there …

Riley.
And this thing was inside of me …
Shit …

Tami.
Did you tell Stokes <u>that</u>?

Tami.
What?

Tami.
That you and I were …

Riley.
No! Of course not … no.
He … no. We haven't really been talking.

Tami.
Not one word?

Riley.
We're casual.
But … no … nothing real.
I've been spending so much time here with you.

Tami.
Who knew we had company that entire time …?

Riley.
You're taking this … not so hard.

Tami.
You expected me to?

Riley.
No [*that's a lie*]… a little.

Tami.
This has nothing to do with me.

Riley.
But it does … in a way.

Tami.
You and I were just …

Riley.
Don't say it.

Tami.
We're not …

Riley.
Is this what you do?

Tami.
Excuse me?

Riley.

What you're doing right now.

Tami.

… standing here talking to you …?

Riley.

No, pull a woman in then drop 'em
like a—

Tami.

Excuse me?!

Riley.

You back away with your hands raised:
"Not my issue."

Tami.

First of all: No, I don't do that.
Second: what's actually happening here
is I'm not letting my emotions
cloud the reality of your baby.
A baby you created with a man
you cheated on with me.

Riley.

=.=

Tami.

=.=

Riley.

I'm sorry.
I'm sorry I said that …
I think I'm just …
I'm terrified … or worried … or …
=.=
=.=
This is supposed to be flipped.

Tami.
What?

Riley.
Stokes was supposed to leave me,
and you were supposed to take me in.
Instead …

Tami.
I'm not leaving you, but Riley …
What would you and I look like in this scenario?
Stokes got rejected from my program, and then
his pregnant girlfriend moves in with me?
That is too HBO even for me …

Riley.
Wow …

Tami.
How would it play out differently?

Riley.
It's about to play out
with me leaving …

Tami.
Listen, we can't—

Riley.
Stop, I don't need to hear—

Tami.
Do you want me to say leave him?

Riley.
=.=

Tami.
Do you want me to say "you and I can raise this
baby?"

Riley.
=.=

Tami.
That doesn't sound ridiculous to you?

Riley.
=.=
=.=
No, it doesn't.

Tami.
=.=
=.=
It doesn't to me either.
=.=
Fuck.

21.

Griffin addresses students (the audience).

Griffin.
Good afternoon. First, I want to thank
Professor Roe for the invitation to speak
with you all today. I never imagined I would
be asked to lead a workshop for graduate students
of architecture, but … here I am doing exactly that.
Today I want to examine with you the intersection of three issues:
gender, ethnicity, and shelter—

Griffin's phone buzzes.

Griffin.
Excuse me. I'm so sorry.

Griffin goes to silence his phone.

Griffin.
I thought I silenced this.
My apologies.

He hesitates when he sees that it's his lawyer calling.

But he silences the call and returns to his lecture admittedly a bit distracted …

> **Griffin.**
> When, when does shelter help someone?
> When does it cause more … more harm than protection?

Griffin sighs, he acknowledges his phone with a glance or a tap [depends where it is].
He veers from his planned remarks to say:

> **Griffin.**
> That … that call I just received was from my lawyer.
> She's supposed to tell me the outcome of a home study.
> It's a visit from a social worker to determine if I'm financially,
> emotionally, and mentally ready to adopt a child. She also inspected my
> home to see if the environment would be safe for a child.
> That call is funny timing because I believe me having the shelter that I
> have,
> caused more harm than good.
> That social worker examined my apartment that I carefully baby-
> proofed.
> And as the visit came to an end she turned to me and asked, "what
> happens when your luck runs out? Do you believe you could raise a
> child, take care of them without the handouts you've received?"

22.

At Griffin's house.

> **Griffin.**
> Fuck.

> **Tami.**
> That social worker is wrong, Griffin.
> Her bias is not your truth.

> **Griffin.**
> It can dictate my truth.
> Even if I got a second opinion, her evaluation
> remains in my file: candidate is <u>not</u> ready to adopt.

Tami.

If your lawyer thinks there's still a window of opportunity,
you should believe in that rather than the report.

Griffin.

Twenty-five years of my life
fucking ripped from me … they
dump me back into society with no
mental or emotional preparation. My apartment is a blessing,
yes, I accept that. I'm grateful for it, but
I had to re-learn how to function …

Tami.

Griffin—

Griffin.

—in ways that that social worker takes for granted.
I had to regain decision-making skills for basic shit—
you know that Tami.

Tami.

I do.

Griffin.

You had to go grocery shopping with me for six months.
You had to call me ten times a day, or else I'd get anxiety attacks
if I didn't have someone to tell me to stop doing "A" to go do "B".
There is no luck in that.
That is fortitude and, and will power and … fuck …
=.=
I'm ready to adopt a child.

Tami.

You still have options.

Griffin.

I finished leading my workshop,
I called my lawyer back who gave me terrible news,
and then Stokes called to tell me Riley's pregnant.

Tami.
=.=

Griffin.
He's having a child and I'm not.
He thinks that baby can fix him and Riley.
I'm listening to him talk and I'm thinking:
it's not a Band-Aid, Stokes. It's your kid …
=.=
And when I found out his Riley is the same Riley that you've been …

Tami.
=.=

Griffin.
Have you talked to that girl?
What is she doing?

Tami.
I don't know.
I keep trying to reason my way out of caring.

Griffin.
What are you doing?
Do you see yourself?

Tami.
=.=
=.=
I do …

Griffin.
You are the most put-together sista I know,
but when it comes to your heart …

Tami.
I know …

Griffin.
You rest your heart in the messiest rooms
of the most troubled homes …

Tami.
Do you really think it's a good time to read somebody?
Like, right now?

Griffin.
If I can't take it out on that social worker,
you're next in line.

Tami.
Great …

Griffin.
=.=
=.=
You're letting yourself get caught up in this …

Tami.
=.=
=.=
I think so …

Griffin.
Why?

Tami.
=.=
=.=
I haven't been painting.

Griffin.
What?

Tami.
I had stopped painting.

Griffin.
For how long?

Tami.
Long enough that the yearning for it had gone stale.

Griffin.
Tami, you didn't tell me about this.

Tami.
What would I say?
I hadn't talked to anybody about it.
=.=
=.=
I had just been carrying this numbness …
in silence.
=.=
And then … Riley … she asked me
about the paintings I made in Brazil …
She showed them to me … and I see my work in her hands.
We slept together that night, and the next morning …
I painted.
=.=
=.=
I've been painting ever since.
=.=
=.=
How can I pull away from that?
From her?
=.=
=.=
Especially now. When she needs me.

Griffin.
You tell me I have options.
I say the same thing to you.
Consider your heart, Tami.
Not what it wants, but what it needs ….

23.

In 1966, G.K. isn't at her typewriter. She doesn't hold pen to paper.
She holds Natalie's hand.

Natalie.
You left.

G.K.
But now I'm back.

Natalie.
You were gone for three weeks.
No trace of you.
When you stepped out, did you intend to come back?

G.K.
I ... I don't know.
I don't think so.

Natalie.
=.=

G.K.
=.=

Natalie.
=.=

G.K.
You cheated on me.

Natalie.
I told you ...

G.K.
You deserve to be left.
I needed to leave you.
Four years of my life I shared with you.

Natalie.
Four beautiful years—

G.K.
Is he the first one?

Natalie.
The first?

G.K.
Have there been others?

Natalie.
What? No!

G.K.
Why did you do this, Nat?

Natalie.
=.=

G.K.
Answer me honestly. Why?

Natalie.
=.=
=.=
I was lonely.
=.=
He was a good friend and I was lonely.
=.=
I just …
=.=
When you moved in with me
you had stopped writing.
The bombing happened in Birmingham
and you couldn't create. It shook you
that those four little girls died like that.
You couldn't justify writing …
=.=
=.=
I fell in love with you, this woman
who made me laugh, made me think.
This woman who did clerical work during the day,
then we helped organize protests at night.
Picket lines, rallies …
We built a life around our beliefs,
our struggles, our happiness…
I felt like I had a real partner.
=.=

Natalie. (continued)
=.=
Then, all of a sudden, you pulled away
from me and went to that typewriter.
=.=
=.=
I know it sounds selfish,
but I was lonely.
I just wanted to be seen.
=.=
I wanted to be in tune with someone.
And Thom, for a moment, was that someone.

G.K. looks at Natalie.

G.K.
My writing is not your enemy.

Natalie.
I never said that.

G.K.
You did—

Natalie.
That's not—

G.K.
If you love me, you'd understand
how important it is for me to do my work…

Natalie.
I do! I do love you …
This baby could be a good thing for us.

G.K.
But what if I didn't want a family?

Natalie.
=.=
Then you can leave again.

G.K.
=.=
=.=
If I did, would you go back to the father?

Natalie.
He's not a father. Stop calling him the father—

G.K.
What if he comes here?

Natalie.
He won't.
He has no reason to.
=.=
Why did you come back?

G.K.
Why do you think I came back?

Natalie.
I hope it's because you love me.
You forgive me. You thank me.
You miss me. You need me.
You want me. This. Us.

G.K.
I love you. I can't forgive you, not yet.
I'm not grateful. I did miss you.
I do need you, which makes me furious, but keeps me lonely.
I do want you. I want what we had.
=.=
You can't raise this child on your own.

Natalie.
Then help me. Stay with me.
Be with us.

24.

Riley stands at Tami's easel.

She admires the view. She takes her phone and snaps a picture.

Tami enters with two glasses.

Tami.
Hey … hey, that's not finished.
No pictures until it's finished.

Riley.
If this is in-progress,
the end-product is going to be amazing.

Tami.
Seltzer for you. Iced tea for me.

Riley.
Thank you.

Tami returns to work on the canvas.

Riley.
Do you have a title yet?

Tami.
Not yet … not until I'm done with it.

Riley watches Tami paint.

Riley.
It's beautiful.
Watching you create is beautiful.
Masterful.

Tami.
If you weren't off liquor,
I'd accuse you of being tipsy…

Riley.
I'm in awe of your work, your beauty.
No liquor necessary, Miss Tami …
=.=

Riley. (continued)
It's been so long since I've watched
someone flow in their destiny.
=.=
Am I the first?

Tami.
The first "what" exactly?

Riley.
The first woman to watch you paint?

Tami.
Nnnno.

Riley.
[*a bit disappointed*]
Oh.
You couldn't lie to me?

Tami.
Do you want to be with a liar?

Riley.
<u>Being</u> a liar, and <u>telling</u> a smart lie
are completely different things …

Tami.
What's the difference?

Riley.
One will get you left,
the other could get you laid.

Tami.
I'll have to remember that …

Riley.
You'd be wise to do so.

They kiss.

Tami pulls away.

Tami.
[*as in "no"*]
Uh-uh.

Riley.
What?

Tami.
If we start this, you'll stay longer,
but you can't stay over,
which makes me very ...

Riley.
Very ...?

Tami.
Unhappy.

Riley.
Who says I can't stay over?

Tami.
Did it go over well last time you
crept home past 3am?

Riley.
=.=

Tami.
We just ... we have to be careful.

Riley.
We just have to be careful with what's happening here.
That's it.
That part of my life isn't about you and me.

Tami.
You forget we have company ... [*touches Riley's stomach*]

Riley steps away.

Tami.
That part of your life is always here.

Riley.
Can I have one conversation with you that doesn't end up being about this baby …
[*she stops herself*]

Tami.
=.=

Riley.
That came out wrong.

Riley.
I don't want my leaving to make you sad.

Tami.
I said unhappy.

Riley.
You meant sad.
You're just afraid to say it.

Tami.
=.=

Riley.
I don't want to go home.
Not yet. Let me stay here. A bit longer.
Then I'll go.
I'll leave in a way that causes you the least "unhappiness".

Tami.
How do you plan to do that?

Riley.
I'll figure it out.

25.

At Griffin's apartment.

Stokes.
G.K. is still alive.
She's just turned 80.
And guess what:
she's living in San Alma.

Griffin.
How did you find that out?

Stokes.
Internet.
We should go visit her.

Griffin.
We?

Stokes.
It's a quick drive.

Griffin.
It's a 2-hour drive.

Stokes.
Why wouldn't you wanna go?
You said she was a big part of
your feminist education, right?
Go visit her to thank her in person.
I just finished *City Streets* and
I have to touch this woman's hand.
I have to.

Griffin.
Riley won't go?

Stokes.
I haven't said anything to her.
She and I … we're still working on us.

Griffin.
The trip might be good for that.

Stokes.
She thinks G.K. is part of our problem.
So … I don't want her to spoil the trip with her … issues.
=.=
You would be the best buddy ever.
I know it.

Griffin.
You think I'm a good buddy, huh?

Stokes.
Yea …

Griffin.
I was in the park earlier today.
And a kid came up to me and said hi.
Smart kid. Great sense of humor.
Wonderful imagination.
His mother came and scooped him up.
I went back to reading my book.
Then, a few minutes later, I hear: Excuse me, buddy.
It's a cop. Someone called the station
and said a "suspicious man" was talking with a kid he "clearly" didn't know.

Stokes.
That's messed up …

Griffin.
They couldn't take me in on anything.
They couldn't give me a ticket.
But I received a "polite" request to leave that section of the park.
So, I guess I am a buddy. A creepy, pervy buddy.

Stokes.
Cops can be idiots…
Most people in general are idiots.
You're a good man.

Griffin.
Thanks.

Stokes.
=.=
=.=
We don't have to go San Alma today.
I just don't want to visit G.K. by myself.
Will you please come with me?

Griffin.
=.=
=.=
Let me think about it.
Maybe after I get over being profiled by a bunch of—

26.

Tami's apartment.

Tami.
Assholes …

Griffin.
I know you really don't
think that, but thank you
for saying it.

Tami.
You can't report someone
for sitting on a bench.

Griffin.
You told me this would happen.
…or you jinxed me.
Either way, you warned me.
And it happened.

Tami.
Most people are
idiots …

Griffin.
Stokes said the same thing.

Tami.
Are you two buddies now?

Griffin.
He called me his buddy, too!

Tami.
For a man who was almost neutered today,
you're in a joking mood.

Griffin.
If I can't laugh at it all, I couldn't get out of bed in the morning …
=.=
Before the park I talked to my lawyer …

Tami.
And?

Griffin.
And she recommended I explore the surrogacy option.
Adoption looks less and less viable.

Tami.
What happened?

Griffin.
I don't look like a father.

Tami.
What?

Griffin.
On paper, to a birthmother, I don't read as a viable option.
An opinion that was basically confirmed
when the cops later chased me away from a park.

Tami.
You just need to make a personal connection.
If a birthmother could get to know you, see how good you are,
she might change her mind.

Griffin.
Maybe.
Thank you for inviting me over for dinner.
I didn't want to be by myself ton—

Keys in a door.
Tami fumbles towards the door.
Griffin is confused.

Griffin.
Who has keys to your apartment?

Riley enters.

Griffin.
=.=

Riley.
Oh … you have company …

Tami.
Hi!

Riley.
Hi …

Tami.
Riley this is Griffin.
Griffin this is …

Griffin.
Hello.

Riley.
Oh … you're …

Griffin.
Yea. And you're …

Tami.
And now everyone is caught up.
Great.

Riley.
I didn't mean to interrupt.

Tami.	**Griffin.**
No, no, no no…	=.=
You're not interrupting.	=.=

Griffin.
Would you like a glass of wine?

Riley.
Oh, I can't … I…

Tami.
Griffin, you know she can't …

Griffin.
Oh, right. Right.
You're expecting.
And you're here.
=.=
At Tami's house.

Tami.
I gave her a key, okay?
Just so she could have a
refuge in case whatever happens.

Griffin.
And where does the child fit into this?

Riley.
[*to avoid further awkwardness*]
I think … I'll just … I'm gonna go
take a shower.

Griffin.
She showers here, too!
A refuge and a bathhouse.

Tami.
[*to Griffin*]
Let's just rain check tonight …

Griffin.
What?
<u>You</u> invited <u>me</u> here for dinner.
<u>That girl</u> pops up, and <u>I</u> get dismissed?

Riley.
"That girl" …?!

Griffin.
[*to Riley*] Stokes told me the two of you are working things out.
And yet you're here.

Riley.
That's between me and him.

Griffin.
And the baby.
And apparently Tami, too.
She's stepping in to co-parent?

Riley.
Jealous?

Griffin.
Excuse me??

Tami.
Stop it … everybody just stop …

Griffin.
What the hell does that mean?

Riley.
I just asked a question—

| **Tami.** | **Riley.** | **Griffin.** |
| Stop it! | I can't ask a question? | You better get your girl, Tami! |

Tami.
Don't make this mess
hotter than it already is. Please.
Griffin—

Griffin.
[*surrenders*]
I'm gone.

Tami.
I'll call you—

Griffin.
Don't bother.
[*To Tami*] I'll keep an eye out for that backbone you lost.

Griffin exits.

27.

In 2014, Stokes works on his novel. He is clearly in a zone. Headphones pump music into his ears.

*In 1966, G.K. still isn't at her typewriter. She doesn't hold pen to paper.
She rubs Natalie's feet.*

The mood is a bit lighter between the women. It's obvious that G.K. is trying hard to play this new role.

Natalie.
What do you think of the name Griffin?
=.=
If it's a boy.

G.K.
After my father?

Natalie.
Yes.

G.K.
=.=

Natalie.
You hate that idea.

G.K.
No …
I like my father. I like that name.
=.=
=.=
I think it's a good idea.
If it's a boy, we'll call him Griffin.

Natalie.
My hands are dry.

G.K.
You're feet are cold, too.
I rub and rub. They stay cold.
That means you'll have a boy.

Natalie.
What?

G.K.
That old wives tale:
dry hands, cold feet means you'll have a boy.

Natalie.
What would happen if it's girl?

G.K.
You'd turn ugly.
A baby girl steals her mother's beauty.

Natalie.
Is that true?
I never heard that before.

G.K.
Time will tell.
But mark my words: it will be a boy.

Natalie.
What if I have a beautiful boy?
What if Griffin is my beautiful baby boy?

G.K.
[*playful*]
Then you'll be cold, dry, and ugly for the next 8 months.

Natalie.
You're awful!

Natalie tickles G.K.

G.K.
[*squeals, laughs*]
No no no no! Natalie Charles, I swear to god I will—
No! Stop!! I hate that! No!

They play around. They lose breath. The playing subsides.
Natalie goes to kiss G.K. who leans in but in the last moment turns away.

Natalie.
=.=

G.K.
=.=

Natalie.
=.=

G.K.
I thought maybe we could go see a movie tonight.
Any requests?

Natalie.
No … I trust you.

G.K.
Good.
=.=
=.=
I'm sorry I just need some time …

Natalie.
I know. You don't have to …

G.K.
I'm back here. With you.
I go to my office job so you could take time off.
I built the crib. I'm rubbing your feet. I'm here for you.
With you. Those are the first steps.
The other steps I need time before I can …

Natalie.
I get it.

In 1966, G.K. exits to a separate room. Natalie's heart sinks.

28.

Stokes drives. Griffin rides in the passenger seat.

Stokes.
Thirteen thousand, seven hundred, and twenty words.
That's how many I have so far.
Do you know the last time I used that many words in a single
document?
Never. Never.

Stokes. (continued)
It's a new personal record.

Griffin.
Congratulations …

Stokes.
And I'm 'bout to smash that bitch later tonight!!

Griffin.
??

Stokes.
The record, I mean.
After we get back from visiting G.K.,
I want to go back to it tonight.

Griffin.
Oh.
Let me know if you ever want a second pair of eyes on it.

Stokes.
Really?

Griffin.
Yea, I'd be happy to read what you have so far.

Stokes.
I might take you up on that.
I gotta admit though: it's so nice to make something for myself.
I'm digging being my own audience, right now.
I've never really done that—made something just for me.
Even with my paintings.
But I appreciate your offer.

Griffin.
No problem. Consider it open-ended.

Stokes.
And thanks, again, for coming with me.

Griffin.

You can stop thanking me.

Stokes.

G.K. is in a pretty nice retirement home.
I wonder how she affords it?

Griffin.

Maybe her family... does she have kids?

Stokes.

Wikipedia didn't mention any.

Griffin.

Maybe a niece or nephew pays for it.

Stokes.

The pictures on the site are nice.
In 60 years, I hope my kid sets me up like *that*.

Griffin.

Start saving now, and they won't have to set you up.
You can set yourself up.

Stokes.

Maybe that's what G.K. did.
She saved up so she could live phat up in "San Alma Silver Condos."

Griffin.

Maybe ...

Stokes.

Where are your folks? They still live out here?

Griffin.

My mother passed five years ago.

Stokes.

I'm sorry to hear that.
That happened while you were locked up?

Griffin.
Yea.

Stokes.
Damn …
Did you get to go to the funer—

Griffin.
[*finality*]
No.

Stokes.
=.=

Griffin.
=.=

Stokes.
=.=

Griffin.
It was just me and her growing up.

Stokes.
=.=
=.=
How did she …?

Griffin.
Cancer. Stomach.

Stokes.
=.=
=.=
What was her name?

Griffin.
Natalie Charles.

Stokes.
Rest in Peace, Natalie Charles.

Griffin.

=.=

=.=

Your parents live out here?

Stokes.

No. They're out east.

=.=

I'm super close to my mom,

but my dad and I never clicked.

=.=

That's weird, right?

He and I never really fell into place with each other.

Griffin.

Why do you think that is?

Stokes.

I don't know.

It's been that way as long as I can remember.

=.=

I used to paint his portrait—over and over.

I think because I kept trying to see him.

Maybe see myself within him.

Griffin.

Did it work?

Stokes.

I'm taking a break from it.

Now I'm writing this novel.

=.=

What made you decide to come with me?

Griffin.

Just a change of heart.

=.=

=.=

Your girlfriend's name is Riley, right ...?

Stokes.

Yea. You should meet her soon.

Things are a bit weird now, but you should come over for dinner.

Once me and her figure out … everything.

Griffin.

Do you have best case, worst case?

Stokes.

What?

Griffin.

The lawyer who worked pro-bono to overturn my case,

he used to have these "best case," "worst case" scenario

brainstorm sessions with me.

It was our way to be prepared for any and everything.

I think that would be a good strategy for you.

Stokes.

Okay …

Griffin.

Like worst case … you and Riley don't work out.

Stokes.

Why wouldn't it work out?

Griffin.

I don't know: you meet somebody else.

Stokes.

But I wouldn't.

Griffin.

But you might.

She might.

Stokes.

Do you think she is?

Griffin.
Maybe. It's a possibility.

Stokes.
You think that baby isn't mine??

Griffin.
Calm down … that's not what I meant.
That is <u>not</u> what I—

Stokes.
Then what?

Griffin.
Okay … Instead of worst case, let's do best—

Stokes.
I don't think I want to play this game, Griffin.
You found this strategy comforting?

Griffin.
I didn't say that. I said it helps to prepare
you, because … anything can really and truly happen.

Stokes.
I Googled you.
So yes, I can see how you believe anything can happen.

Griffin.
You finally did the Google…

Stokes.
I read those charges. Shit.
Kidnap and murder.

Griffin.
It wasn't me.

Stokes.

I know …

That's terrifying though.

To have the whole world say it's you.

Griffin.

It wasn't the <u>whole</u> world.

Tami believed me.

My first lawyer believed me.

Even though he couldn't defend for shit.

My mother knew I was innocent, too.

Stokes.

If I had known you back then,

I would've believed you.

Griffin.

You were a baby when I got locked up.

Stokes.

A toddler. I was a toddler.

And kids are hyper perceptive.

They got that sixth sense.

The men fall silent.

Stokes contemplates, then:

Stokes.

Best case: I'm a great partner to Riley.

And I'm a great father to our child.

=.=

Worst case: I'm a great father to my child that I created with my ex.

=.=

Either way I'm a great father.

That's a win / win.

29.

In 1966, G.K. enters with a suitcase. She packs up the last of her papers. She packs up her typewriter. She's a bit rushed.

In 2014, Tami rubs Riley's feet. The women are peaceful and content.
Riley freestyles on a beat she created.

Riley.
Drop some fire, Tami.

Tami.
Excuse me?

Riley.
Jump on this beat, right quick.

Tami.
I don't think so.

Riley.
Come on ...
[*ad-libs some hype man lingo*]
Oh! What? Yea!
Drop it in the booth!
[*etc*]

Tami laughs.

She decides to go for it.

Tami freestyles a verse.
It's actually pretty good!!

Riley is surprised.

In 2014, Riley and Tami trade verses like Salt-n-Pepa.

In 1966, G.K. places a handwritten note for Natalie to read. G.K. gathers her things.
She walks out on Natalie.

In 2014, Tami and Riley have somehow ended up singing the song lyrics from the end of
Tennessee by Arrested Development.

In 1966, Natalie enters the apartment with a bouquet of flowers.

Natalie.
Gina, I'm home!

Tami & Riley.
[*rap and sing*]

Natalie.
Gina, you here?

Tami & Riley.
[*laugh, rap*]

In 1966, Natalie finds G.K.'s letter.
Natalie reads in silence for several moments, then:

Natalie.
[*reads aloud*]
"...I make this choice now,
so that I break only one heart instead of two.
I can't be a part of this family. I'm sorry."

Riley orchestrates a pretty dope end to the song.

The women celebrate their jam session as Natalie crumbles to the floor, devastated.

30.

In 2014, G.K Marche is in her early 80s.
She looks good for her age.
People often assume she's in her 50s.

Stokes is in awe.
Griffin is engaged.
The conversation is easy, light.
G.K. is fantastic. Quick-witted, charming.

G.K.
... I spent years just ... seeing the world.
In the late 60s, I traveled around Europe.
In the 70s, I spent time in Africa.
In the 80s, I was all over North America.

G.K. (continued)
And the writing never stopped.
Those were the years when the stories …
[*G.K. rubs her hands*]
I could write anywhere, any time.
I carried these tiny notebooks with me.
I used to be so … rigid, you know?
Couldn't leave my typewriter for too long.
Could only write at my desk. Blah, blah, blah …
But when I left the city in the 60s … I had to find a way
to create while in motion.
And, shit, that damn typewriter I lugged around was heavy.

The men laugh.

G.K.
You young boys don't know about that, but those shits were hea.vy.
You press those keys, you needed muscle in your hands.
Now you have those itty bitty laptops. I bet your hands are weak.
[*to Griffin*] Give me your hand.

Griffin does.
G.K. feels for the muscle in Griffin's hand.

G.K.
See, look at that … weak hands.

Stokes laughs.
He is having the best time.

Stokes.
What about me?

G.K. feels Stokes' hand.

G.K.
=.= [*feels*]
=.= [*feels*]
You paint?
I thought you said you were a writer.

Stokes.
I am … I'm writing a novel now,
but … well, I've been painting for a long time.
How did you …?

G.K.
It's in the muscle.
=.=
You might do alright at the typewriter.
Strong hands.
Maybe you can come visit me again,
you can paint my portrait?

Stokes.
I would … yes! Absolutely!
I would love to.

G.K.
Remind me your names again?

Stokes.
Stokes.

G.K.
Stokes and …

Griffin.
Griffin.

G.K.
Griffin … that was my daddy's name.
He was a good man, which means you must be a good man, too.

Griffin.
I try to be.

G.K.
You know my work?

Griffin.

Yes, ma'am.

And I love every word of it.

The way you describe Lila trying to escape

That riot in <u>The Fall</u>

Is masterful.

G.K.

[*smiles*]

You can come back and visit me, too.

=.=

=.=

[*studies his face*]

I keep thinking I've seen you somewhere before …

Are you a writer, too? A painter?

Griffin.

No, ma'am.

I'm an avid reader.

G.K.

=.= [*looks at Griffin*]

=.= [*recognizes … something*]

You feel familiar for some reason.

Stokes.

Maybe you've seen his picture on the news?

In a magazine?

G.K.

It's not that kind of familiar …

It's like the remix of an original song.

Your face isn't a face I know, but … I know those … features.

Griffin.

=.=

Stokes.

=.=

G.K. looks at Griffin as if recognizing the first notes of a sad song.

She knows who this man is.
Her expression changes—a flash of shock, sadness, awe, disbelief.

Stokes.
Are you alright, ma'am?

G.K. breaks her gaze from Griffin just as swiftly as she caught it. She flashes a smile to cover her truth.

G.K.
Yes, yes, darling, I am fine.
Sometimes the memories get stuck together.
And it takes me a minute to …
[*looks at both men*]
I must be thinking of someone else.

Griffin.
I wish I could be helpful…

G.K.
No need to entertain this creaky mind.
I packed so many things up here over the years.
Ideas for a great line, a great story, a great scene, a great face …

Stokes.
Do you still write?

G.K.
Everyday.
You?

Stokes.
Yea … for almost three weeks.
I hope to finish it before the baby comes.

G.K.
You're expecting!
That's fantastic.

Griffin.
Do you have any children?

G.K.
Yes, I met my partner in '86.
She had three young ones from a previous marriage.
She and I raised them.
So, yes, I have three children and … six grandchildren.
You?

Griffin.
No, not yet.
I'm trying to.

G.K.
You're trying to?

Griffin.
My options are limited, but …
I'm hopeful.

G.K.
[*to Stokes*]
Your friend is cryptic.

Stokes.
He can be.

Griffin.
I'd rather not get into it if that's okay.
It's a problem that sits heavy inside of me,
and it isn't something I want to talk about.

G.K.
=.=

Stokes.
=.=

G.K.
Okay.
=.=
=.=
Alright.

G.K. (continued)
=.=
=.=
That's fine.

Griffin.
I'm sorry.

G.K.
No need to apologize.

Stokes.
Griffin, it's okay.

Griffin.
=.= [*tears fill his eyes*]
=.=

Griffin flicks away the tears while trying to stop them from coming.

Without hesitation, G.K. takes Griffin's hand, a comforting gesture.

Stokes is unsure what to do. Griffin continues to fight tears.

G.K. comforts Griffin.

Stokes is silent.

31.

Griffin and Stokes drive back home.
The men are silent.
Griffin looks out the window.
Stokes drives. Sneaks glances at Griffin to make sure he's okay.

Silence for a while.

Griffin.
I'm ... sorry if I embarrassed you.

Stokes.
You didn't.

Griffin.
=.=

Stokes.
=.=

Griffin.
Who cries?
What is that?

Stokes.
It's okay.

Griffin.
I didn't come with
the intention to weep in G.K. Marche's arms.

Stokes.
I'm sure you didn't.

Griffin.
=.=

Stokes.
=.=

Griffin.
I miss my mother.

Stokes.
=.=

Griffin.
When G.K. touched my hand …
I felt my mother's.

Stokes.
=.=

Griffin.
=.=

Stokes.
=.=

Griffin.
That's weird, right?

Stokes.
It's a bit weird, yes.

Griffin.
It felt weird.
What's that about?

Stokes.
It was a motherly thing she did to you.
I watched her comfort you.
She looked like a mother next to you.
=.=
=.=
I tried to see Riley like that.
As a mother comforting someone.
=.=
=.=
I couldn't see it.

Griffin.
[*slips out*]
I had the same thought when
I met her.
[*freeze*]
[*fuck*]

Stokes.
You met her?

Griffin.
Who?

Stokes.
Riley.

Griffin.
Riley …?

Stokes.
My girlfriend.

Griffin.
Oh …

Stokes.
You said you met her.

Griffin.
Did I?

Stokes.
You did.
When did you meet her?

Griffin.
=.= [*decides to fess up*]
You remember when I left you the message
saying I'd ride up with you to meet G.K.?

Stokes.
Yes.

Griffin.
Right before I made that call.

Stokes.
Why didn't you tell me?

Griffin.
I planned to.
I decided to come with you because I wanted
the chance to talk to you about …

Stokes.
About what?

Griffin.
You.
You and Riley.
And the baby.

Stokes.
What about us?

Griffin.
If you want to be with her …
If you want to raise that baby with her …
you need to have a real talk with her soon.

Stokes.
Griffin, where did you meet Riley?

32.

Split scene:

Tami. Are you trying to fuck this up more than it already is?	**Stokes.** =.=
Griffin. Look, I didn't have to tell you anything.	**Riley.** I didn't mean for any of this to happen.
Tami. Just like you didn't have to tell Stokes— I have to call Riley.	**Stokes.** What, us? The baby? Or Tami?
Griffin. What are you doing? Why would you do that?	**Riley.** I don't know. All of it. Some of it? I don't know …

Tami.
[*cellphone in hand*]
I want to make sure she's okay.
[*presses the screen a few times*]

Griffin.
Don't call her, Tami.

Tami.
Griffin, your right to be heard
is revoked. I can't believe you.

Griffin.
He deserved to know that
he should be worried.

Tami.
Riley told you she would handle it.

Griffin.
By hiding out at your house?

Tami.
You need to get a kid stat.
Preoccupy you with someone else's
life you can destroy.

Griffin.
That is a low blow, Tami.

Tami.
[*leaves a message*]
Hey, it's me.
Call me when you get this.

Stokes.
You cheated on me.

Riley.
I never meant to
hurt you.

Stokes.
Do you love her?
[*Riley's cellphone rings*]

Stokes.
Is that her?

Riley.
I have other people
in my life besides
you and—

Stokes.
Let me see the
phone.

Riley.
No. [*ignores Tami's
call*]

Stokes.
Fuck, really? Is this
how it is now?
Four years and all
of a sudden you
treating me like an
afterthought?

Tami. (continued)
Griffin told me what he did.
I want to make sure you're okay.
[*ends the call*]

Tami paces.
Griffin watches her.

Riley.
[*phone buzzes again*]

Stokes.
She left a message?
Maybe I should go over
there.

Tami.
Maybe I should go over there.

Griffin.
You're not going over there.
Tami, stop.
Stop this.
You leaving this apartment
is not a smart move.

Riley.
You're not going over there.
Stokes, stop.
Stop this.

Stokes.
Then talk to me.

Tami.
=.=

Riley.
=.=

Griffin.
Let them work it out.

Stokes.
Talk to me.
Riley …

Riley exits, Stokes follows.
Griffin and Tami remain in their scene.

Tami.
Yea, that was the original plan, Griffin: Let Riley work it out.
Then you went to Stokes and started running your mouth.

Griffin.
Tami, I told you—

Tami.

I know. Right.

It was an "accident" but the "universe"

was gonna reveal the truth one way or the other …

I swear, you and this …

Iyanla Van-Can't lifestyle you

lead is …

you can't force the way you live on everybody else.

Griffin.

"Iyanla Van-Can't"?

What the hell are you talking about, Tami.

And I don't force anything on anybody.

Tami.

I shoulda known … when you left my apartment after meeting Riley.

I should've seen this coming …

Griffin.

Seen what coming?

Tami.

I start to have something in my life that makes me happy,

has me fulfilled—

Griffin.

[*scoffs*]

That girl fulfills you?

Tami.

See, that, that attitude right there.

There was never any chance you would let me

be happy with Riley.

Griffin.

Uhh, Tami, Riley was never gonna let you be happy with Riley.

Step back and take an honest look at her situation.

How can you build a life around deceit?

Tami.
We weren't building a life. She and I were just
spending time together—that's it.

Griffin.
And she needs keys to your apartment to spend time with you?

Tami.
This is why—
[*she stops herself*]

Griffin.
This is why, what?

Tami.
=.=

Griffin.
Tami?

Tami.
Griffin, I think you should leave.
If I let my rage pilot this conversation,
I will definitely say things that will hurt us both.
And I don't want to do that.

Griffin.
Say whatever you have to. Say it. As long as you speak your truth,
we'll get past the pain—

Tami.
That. That shit, right there, when you
say shit like that—it just… stop being a fucking
emotionally aware Black feminist all the damn time,
and see me Griffin. Your best-fucking-friend, Tami Sterling-Brown.
Talk to me like a regular fucking human being!
Stop being so conscious and just see me.
=.=
=.=
It had been almost three years since I stopped painting.
=.=

Tami. (continued)

=.=

=.=

Do you know what happened three years ago?

Griffin.

=.=

Tami.

The testimony that convicted you
got thrown out as insufficient.
And you and I started the journey to get you free.

=.=

We thought you would die in that prison, Griffin.
We never talked about it, but I knew we had come to terms with the
possibility of that.
And then that testimony got thrown out.

Griffin.

Are you upset about that?

Tami.

No! No, no, absolutely not. I thank God everyday
that you got your justice. So many others don't,
but you did. I am so grateful for that.

Griffin.

Then what are you saying, Tami?

Tami.

I'm saying … if I'm honest with
myself—with both of us:
your freedom trapped me.

Griffin.

=.=

Tami.

=.=

Griffin.
=.=

Tami.
It did.
When your mother passed, I picked up the fight
to keep that connection with you. To sustain your line
to the outside world. And I took that torch with pride
and determination but there were sacrifices, Griffin.

Griffin.
I know …
I know that …

Tami.
And when that testimony got thrown out …
I put everything I had into getting your freedom.
=.=
I'm not claiming Riley to be a savior or anything.
I know how complicated it is … but the time
I have with her … it's mine … it's something she and I have.
And I haven't shared that type of … with any other woman in a long
time.
In a really long time. And, I know it was my choice not to get serious
with other women after I escaped that nightmare with Stevie. I know
that.

Griffin.
Tami…

Tami.
And I'm not angry at you, Griffin.

Griffin.
I get it …

Tami.
I just need you to see me where I'm at right now,
and see where I've been.

Griffin.
I get it.

He goes to her. Takes her hand or makes some other comforting/compassionate gesture.

Tami may weep. Or she may simply exhale a deep and profound release, grateful that she can feel that Griffin does indeed "get it" and his gesture is safe and understanding and is specifically for Tami Sterling-Brown in her present messy, complicated, and raw self.

33.

In 1967, Natalie comforts baby Griffin. She cradles him in her arms.
She hums a melody: Thelonius Monk or John Coltrane.

Natalie.
I know … mommy knows.
Those teeth are coming in whether you like it or not.
My baby Griffin is hurting, I know …

Natalie's continues to hum. A fussy Griffin eventually calms. The phone rings. Natalie answers it without missing a beat in her comforting of baby Griffin.

Natalie.
Hello, *Sewn by Natalie*, this is Natalie speaking.
=.=
Yes, ma'am, your friend is right:
I am the best Black seamstress in The Bay.
=.=
Two suits and four sundresses?
That's fine.
Can you come by the shop here so I can do measurements and pricing?
=.=
In 20 minutes? That's fine. I'll see you soon.

Natalie hangs up the phone. Returns to humming a song for Griffin, then:

Natalie.
How's my little man?
You wanna try and take a nap for mommy?

34.

The park.

Riley and Tami are seeing each other for the first time in—

Riley.
It's been weeks since we've seen each other ...

Tami.
=.=

Riley.
I hope you understand it's not what I want.
I want to see you. But I have to work through things with Stokes.
We have to figure out what it means: raising this child ...
and we have to decide how he and I function within that ...

Tami.
So you're staying with him?

Riley.
=.=
He's the father. And he wants to be the father.
And I think he'll be a blessing in the baby's life.
He and I, we just ...

Tami.
What about you?

Riley.
=.=

Tami.
Is this what you want?

Riley.
=.=
Most of my life I've always known what I wanted.
My mother said I came into the world holding a checklist.
=.=
This is the first time my certainty ... keeps moving, shifting ...

Riley. (continued)
=.=
I want … I want to treat this kid well, take care of 'em, be good to 'em.

Tami.
You will.

Riley.
=.= [*a slight smile*]
You'd be a good mother.

Tami.
Me?

Riley.
Yea, you don't think so?

Tami.
[*sarcastic*]
There's only so many hours in the day
to live life who can squeeze in mothering …?

Riley.
You talk like it's a hobby …

Tami.
For some people it is.

Riley.
That's not you, tho.

Tami.
No? What makes you so sure?

Riley.
I just know it.

Tami.
=.=
You remember that painting you pointed out on my office wall?

Riley.
Yea.

Tami.
Stevie is the ex who painted it.
She gave it to me as a promise
that she would never put her hands on me again.

Riley.
=.=

Tami.
And I accepted it.
I took her back and accepted that painting.

Riley.
And did she keep her promise?

Tami.
No. No she didn't.
=.=
I thought I wanted to raise a family with Stevie.
I loved her. And I thought she could be a good mother.
We could be better to each other if she and I had a ...
But it didn't work out like that.
=.=
When I finally got the courage to leave
I called Griffin's mom in tears.
She was like a mother to me.
I told her what happened. She listened to me with no judgment.
She paid for a one-way flight from Philly back here to The Bay.
And she let me sleep on her couch for months.
When Stevie called, Natalie told her to fuck off.
=.=
That woman was so good to me when I probably didn't deserve it.

Riley touches Tami's hand.
Tami accepts it.

Tami.

You're the first woman I've ... been close to who's having a kid.
For the first time, I was feeling the real possibility of motherhood in my life.
I'd be at the office,
in my car, in bed with you,
imagining what it would be like,
what having a child could look like ... for me.
=.=
=.=
I shouldn't wait for you while you figure things out with Stokes, should I?

Riley.
=.=

Tami.
I shouldn't.

Riley.
It's unfair for me to say one way or the other.
But ... you shouldn't.
=.=
=.= (*kisses Tami's hand*)

Tami squeezes Riley's hand in return.

35.

Griffin sits with G.K. at her retirement home.

Griffin.
I'm not one to make surprise visits ...

G.K.
Griffin, I told you it's fine.

Griffin.
I gave you a bit of notice.

G.K.

You did. And I appreciate it.

Griffin.

It was an impulse on my part.
The decision to drive here.

G.K.

Why are you still explaining what's already come to be?

Griffin.

I just needed … I needed to call on someone.
I thought of you.

G.K.

I'm glad you did.
=.=
I really am … Griffin.
If you needed someone, I'm glad
you chose me.

Griffin.

I rented a coupe to drive here.
It took 15 minutes to get a $45,000 car.
It's been almost 30 years since I've been behind the wheel.
My credit card has a fifteen-hundred dollar limit.
But they let me have the keys.
And now I'm here.
=.=
=.=
I applied for a loan to help cover the cost of a surrogacy.
=.=
I got turned down. Not enough collateral.

G.K.

I'm so sorry.

Griffin.

A child is not a car rental.

G.K.

It is not.

Griffin.

I have access to money from my mom's insurance policy.
I earmarked those funds to help raise a kid. My kid.
It didn't even occur to me that money would get eaten up
by the attempt to simply have one.
=.=
At this point, it's cheaper to fall in love.
=.=
Your poem sits in my heart today.
 [*recites G.K.'s poem*]
"A universe blooms inside you.
I wait. I am patient next to you at night as we rest in bed.
I am patient as I type. As you thread.
We wonder how long.
How long before this house of string collapses from the weight of our silence?
I write an instructional poem: how to catch creation.
I type the steps: one, two, three, four, and so on.
You glance at the paper, then say to me: there are no instructions here.
Only a list of numbers.
I tell you I know.

Griffin & G.K.

"… It's a sheet to take notes in case I meet someone who has the answers."

Griffin.

That poem came to me this morning.
I had to call on you, G.K.

G.K. touches Griffin's hand in a moment of comfort.

G.K.

That insurance policy from your mother.
Does that mean she passed away …?

Griffin.
Yes, ma'am.
Several years ago.

This is news to G.K. She sits stunned as a wave of memories casts a shadow across her face.

G.K.
=.=
=.=
I'm sorry for … your loss.

Griffin.
Thank you.
She was a good woman.
A good mother.

G.K.
… who raised a good man.

The seeker and giver of comfort are muddled in this moment.

G.K.
I am so grateful the universe
made a way to bring us together, Griffin.

*Griffin smiles. Grateful to have this much-needed love
from an elder.*

*For G.K. this moment, this news about Natalie brings forth the following memory for
G.K.*

We watch as G.K. stands from Griffin and steps into this moment in …

35a.

*1988, Natalie waits at a bus stop. Although twenty years have passed since we last saw
her, she doesn't look much older. There is, however, a deep exhaustion that encases her
spirit.*

Natalie patiently waits for the bus. Quietly, a bit timidly, G.K. approaches her. Natalie doesn't notice her at first. G.K. stands there a bit nervous. Finally:

G.K.
Natalie …?

Natalie looks. A slight shock.
Then a small smile.

The women fall into a moment of awkwardness.
Do they hug? Shake hands?

Natalie.
Gina …

G.K.
I saw you from across the street.
I wanted to come over and say hey.
It's… it's good to see you. It's been awhile. Twenty years …?

Natalie.
Something like that.
=.=
It has been a long time.
=.=
How … how have you been?

G.K.
I've been … ok.

Natalie.
You're not back in the Bay, are you?

G.K.
No, I'm in L.A.
I just bought a house with my part…ner.

Natalie.
Oh.

G.K.
Yea, and …

Natalie.
That's nice.

G.K.
I'm in town for a book tour. I'm reading at The Alley Bookstore this evening.

Natalie.
From the First Look, to the Final Goodbye.

G.K. is surprised that Natalie knows about her latest book.

G.K.
Yea, that's the one …

Natalie.
I hope it goes well.

G.K.
You should come this evening if you can.

Natalie.
I can't …

G.K.
Oh. Alright.

Natalie.
Today's my day to visit Griffin.
I usually don't get back until late.
I have to take public transportation to him.
No car.

G.K.
Where is he?

Natalie.
Grover Hill.

G.K.
The prison?

Natalie.
Yes.

G.K.
Natalie, what happened?

Natalie.
He's innocent.

G.K.
Okay. Alright.

Natalie, without warning, bursts into tears. G.K., without hesitation, comforts her.

Natalie.
I'm, I'm sorry to …

G.K.
You're fine. You shouldn't apolo…

Natalie steps away.
A moment passes between the women; they transcend any past hurt
to be present and care about each other in a genuine way.

G.K.
I … I have my car. Do you want a ride?
I can at least take you out there, drop you off.

Natalie.
I'm fine. You don't have to …

G.K.
I know. But I want to.

Natalie.
=.=

G.K.
=.=

Natalie.
=.=
=.=
Alright. Okay. Thank you, Gina.

36.

Stokes isn't typing at his laptop.
He isn't staring at a blank canvas.

He stands facing Riley.

Stokes.
You left.

Riley.
But now I'm back.

Stokes.
You were gone for a week.
What the fuck, Riley.

Riley.
I'm fine.

Stokes.
No, you're not.
Clearly you have lost your damn mind.
What the fuck?

Riley.
The baby is fine.

Stokes.
I almost filed a report.
Called our families.

Riley.
What stopped you?

Stokes.
Tami stopped me.

Riley.
=.=

Stokes.
She stopped me.
I went to her house in a rage.
I thought you were there.

Riley.
I wasn't.

Stokes.
I found that out.
She didn't know where you were either.
But she sent you a text.
And you replied.

Riley.
=.=

Stokes.
I had been calling you non-stop for two days.
And you write back to Tami in two minutes.
"I'm fine. Staying with my friend in San Rey."
=.=
=.=
She showed me your message.
I sat on her couch. And I couldn't move.
It felt like my heart was climbing up my throat.
=.=
Tami sat with me while I caught my breath.
Tami did that.
She called Griffin to come over.
And they sat up with me all night.
=.=

Stokes. (continued)
=.=
Why did you disappear on me?

Riley.
I needed space.
To think …

Stokes.
We agreed: no more distance;
no more silence…

Riley.
I know…

Stokes.
Then why disappear?
My baby's coming in a few months, Riley.

Riley.
It's just yours? Nobody else's?
Our baby. It's <u>our</u> baby, Stokes.

Stokes.
Is this how it's gonna be?
You coming and going whenever you feel like it—

Riley.
No…

Stokes.
How can I trust that?

Riley.
Because I came back.
I'm back. I'm here.
I want to raise a good kid. With you.

Stokes loves this woman. He can't help it.

Stokes.
=.=
=.=
We will.

Riley.
Regardless of what happens with us …?

Stokes.
=.=
Yes.
=.=
=.=
Can I show you something?

Stokes retrieves his phone and pecks on the screen a few times to pull up a document.

Stokes.
Griffin helped me draft a plan.
It's a list of things you and I should start thinking about.
It's just a draft. We can develop it … together.

37.

Griffin sits with Tami in his apartment.

Griffin.
G.K. said she knew my mother.

Tami.
What …?

Griffin.
Yea.

Tami.
Wow …

Griffin.
Small world, I know, right?

Tami.
The queer scene has been incestuous for decades and decades …

Griffin.
What does that mean?

Tami.
You don't think G.K. and your mom smashed back in the day?

Griffin.
Tami—

Tami.
Come on …

Griffin.
I love you, but you if you talk about my mom smashing again, we gonna have to exchange some words, Tami.

Tami.
How does G.K. know her?

Griffin.
She didn't finish telling me.
Her grandkids showed up and interrupted our Skype session.

Tami.
To be continued …

Griffin.
Definitely.
But it makes sense, tho—G.K. knowing my mom.

Tami.
Why is that?

Griffin.
When she touches my hand, it feels like home.

Tami.
Well … maybe because you know her writing.
You feel close to her through her words.

Griffin.
No … it's not that.

Tami.
Maybe you just hate men?

Griffin.
What?

Tami.
You spent all those years locked up with 'em.
Maybe you're parched for all sorts of connection with
any type of woman.

Griffin.
You make me sound loose …

Tami.
Not that type of connection, Griffin.
You know what I mean.

Griffin.
I don't know … you're so obsessed with smashing …

Tami.
I am not obsessed!

Griffin.
And I don't hate men.
I like Stokes.

Tami.
Stokes is different.

Griffin.
How?

Tami.
It's hard not to like somebody who listens to you.
Looks up to you.

Tami. (continued)
He's like the favorite nephew you never had.

Griffin.
You think he looks up to me?

Tami.
He's calling you for co-parenting advice.

Griffin.
Just because I give it, doesn't mean he takes it.

Tami.
It's good advice.

Griffin.
You think so?

Tami.
It is.

Griffin.
Says the woman with no children.

Tami.
By choice.
I have no children by choice.
If you only knew how many women
wanted to raise a family with me ...

Griffin.
How many?

Tami.
Like, three or four.
The most recent being Miss Riley.
But it's a good thing it won't happen.
Watching Stokes weep on my couch somehow makes
his baby mama less attractive to me.

Griffin.

That was a good thing you did for him, Tami.
Taking care of Stokes when he showed up at your apartment.

Tami.

Yea ... well ...

Griffin.

You know who would've done that same exact thing?

Tami.

You.

Griffin.

Besides me.

Tami.   **Griffin.**

=.=   My mother.
Your mother.

Tami.

True ... true.

Griffin.

Did I tell you G.K. and I have started writing sessions on Skype?
She thinks I should write a memoir.

Tami.

Oh yea?

Griffin.

Yea.

Tami.

[*mock excitement*]
Oh, did I tell you ...

Griffin.

[*genuine excitement*]
What?

Tami.
[*mock*]
I just acquired a bunch of free time to be
alone and devastated by my life choices!

Griffin.
You have me, Tami.

Tami.
And now you have Stokes, his baby, G.K. …
Before you know it, you'll end up being Riley's doula.

Griffin.
You carry a razor under that tongue?

Tami.
I came here to talk to you,
and you end up making me more depressed.

Griffin.
Is that possible?

Tami.
Shut up.

Griffin.
What did you want to talk to me about?

Tami.
=.=
=.=
What, what type of writing prompts does G.K. give you?

Griffin.
Last session, she told me to write about my earliest memory.

Tami retrieves a sketchpad and pencil from her tote.
She opens it to a fresh page.

Griffin.
What are you doing?

Tami.
G.K. is encouraging you to write your past.
You and I can work on the future.

Griffin.
What?

Tami.
Let's sketch an album of possibility, Griffin, right now.

Griffin.
An album of possibility?

Tami.
Yes.

Griffin.
And what will we put inside this possibility?

Tami.
A baby.
For this, you and I are going to create a baby.

She sketches.

Griffin.
This is nice …

Tami.
It's just a line, Griffin.

Griffin.
No, I mean it's nice to see you
drawing. Look at you …

Tami.
Alright. Okay. Break it up …

Tami sketches.
Griffin looks on.
He can't help but smile.

Griffin.
You've gotten better at figure drawing.

Tami.
Does this mean you'll cooperate?

Griffin.
Ah, is this the newborn portrait?

Tami.
With the little cap and swaddled in a blankie.

Tami continues to sketch with Griffin offering guidance and support.
It turns into a joyous moment of creation between two close friends.
Riley enters the playing space with her beat machine and begins to build a beat from
scratch. Stokes enters, carrying his laptop. He crosses to Riley and touches her belly—a
moment of warm exchange.

Stokes sits with his laptop and continues work on his novel.

The beat that Riley builds matures as the following montage appears on stage:

In 1967, Natalie enters with a sleeping baby Griffin in her arms. She places him in a
bassinet. Turns her focus to cutting / folding / sewing fabrics.
In 1966, G.K. types at her typewriter.
In present day, Stokes types at his laptop.
In present day, G.K., in her 80s, types at her typewriter.

The stage is filled with past and present creation of memory.
The creation of happiness, sadness, and resilience.

One by one a moment of creation fades away.

Griffin and Tami remain.

They continue to laugh and enjoy the creation of possibility.

Griffin.
It's a girl?

Tami.
It is a girl.
You okay with that?

Griffin.
She's perfect.

Griffin watches the image that Tami sketches.
Eventually he watches her sketch.

Tami continues to work on the image, lost in the possibility of it.

Griffin smiles, returns his attention to the pad.

Tami.
Maybe it wouldn't be so crazy.

Griffin.
What's that?

Tami.
If I carried one of these for a few months.

Griffin looks at Tami.

Tami.
=.= [*sketches*]

Griffin.
Are you …?

Tami.
=.= [*sketches*]

Griffin.
Are you serious?

Tami.
It's not such a horrible idea.

Griffin.
=.=

Tami.
=.=

Tami stops sketching and looks to Griffin.

Tami.
=.=
=.=
I think I want to have a kid.

end of play.

hollow roots

a play for one performer

<u>Players:</u>

     Late 20s. To be performed by a person who identifies as a Black American woman.

<u>Time:</u>

     The near future.

<u>Place:</u>

     An urban metropolis similar to New York City.

i pay $150 every month for unlimited access to the city's public transportation. anywhere within a 400-mile radius i can ride the automated metro, the bus, streetcars, motos, the ferry, cable transit, and the second-hand puddle jumpers as many times as i want. for $150 every month. i used to catch the Q13 bus 2 blocks from my place and go 8 miles east to my job. that's what i used to use my unlimited access for. but things have changed.

it's inevitable. change. the only thing constant is change. prayer changes everything. life changes for the better. you got some change you can spare? i need a change in my life.

see, the thing about 'change' is that it never arrives by itself. depending on what kind it is, it'll show up at your house with one or two people, or a whole bunch of folks. but understand and believe: change is the one running the show.

before & after may lay up in your bed.
disorientation will drink the last of your apple juice.
elation might forget to raise the toilet seat.
and loneliness might drain your cell phone battery

but

change can lift you up or wipe you out.
change can press that button at anytime.

and i hate that bastard sonofabitch something fierce.

now, i don't use that word very often: hate.

the first time i remember hearing it was when one of my mother's students—she gave private violin and cello lessons—when one of her students had a meltdown while struggling through a difficult series of notes. this student of hers was a chunky white girl with long brown hair. she wore big green plastic frames that held plastic lenses. i remember that detail only because her glasses looked like candy to me. like sour apple jolly ranchers. and as a four-year-old, that's how i decided i liked people—if they made me think of candy.

you remember being that age when everything looked like a good time? you could see a toy in the blandest bits the world had to offer. any object held the potential of laughter. all you had to do was reach out and play with it.
yea.

those paperback books are bricks to build a podium.
that big cardboard box is an airplane.
that mixing bowl is a helmet.

her glasses were sour apple jolly ranchers.
and she had a meltdown while trying to play the following:

> [*sings the melody of a complicated series of notes. hits a flat note to indicate a mistake. pause. start from the beginning. sings the melody of complicated notes. hits the same flat note again. pause. repeat same mistake*]

and i remember her saying, 'i can't play this stupid song. i hate my fat fingers. they won't reach the right notes. i haaaayyytte them.'

the way she said that word, 'haaaayyytttte,' sounded so true to me. my four-year-old ears heard that word and my four-your-old brain was thinking, 'that white girl is for real about not liking her fingers.'

my father told me: say what you mean to say in the best way you can say it.

sour apple jolly rancher said what she meant to say.

and i try to do the same thing, too. lesson learned from her and my father.

i live life, trying to hold onto these memories. certain ones are faded. others are fading. and then there are memories that sit in between my lips and leap into the air like this:

one day, last summer, early afternoon, i stepped off a streetcar and started walking towards my doctor's office. while waiting for the crosswalk signal to change a smiling brown woman handed me a menu. a new fusion restaurant just opened not far from my destination. after my doctor poked me and nodded his head and scribbled his findings on a clipboard, i still had time for lunch. a glance at the menu … decent selections ... prices aren't so bad. i decided to check it out.

i arrived at the restaurant, stepped inside and the place felt like that feeling you get when you discover the sweet spot on a new lover. the hostess greeted me with a smile so warm it made me want to hug her, but i kept myself in check. we did the

'how many?'
'just one.'

'just one?'
'just one.'

exchange. and i followed her to a large table where 5 people were already seated. she extended her arm to indicate i should sit in the only empty seat left.

i mistook 'family style' to mean 'home cooking.'
to mean 'owned and operated by a loving family'
but
'family style' meant 'communal seating' and heaping mounds of ethnic edibles and pitchers of light pink drinks with chunks of fruit floating on top.

i wanted to turn around, tell them 'no thank you, but best of luck to you and your family's endeavor' and then
i heard laughter coming from the back of the restaurant. i looked and discovered it was coming from the kitchen.

people say 'so and so has a great laugh'
the kind of person whose laugh is contagious.

but what i heard coming from that kitchen was … a cardboard box that i could turn into an airplane or a race car.

[*as if hearing it again*]

… a milk jug that becomes a tugboat.
bottle caps are computer keys …

i found out that laughter belonged to the head chef.
and with that information, i sat in the empty chair and placed the blue cotton napkin across my lap. i wanted that laughter for lunch, even if i did have to sit with a group of strangers.

we were all dressed in that bottom-rung corporate attire. and each of us had that reputation at work for being 'the quiet one.' lunch and coffee breaks were taken alone spent reading a book just thick enough to feel invested or sitting in the public courtyard watching people go about their daily routines.

all of us had passions. our day jobs kept us civilized but our hobbies, talents, and dreams made the blood pump, helped keep our vision clear so we could see the bullshit our day jobs were steeped in.

six brown bodies sat around that family style table. and while our skin tones held similar hues, i felt the specifics of our ethnic make-ups had few strands in common. we didn't get into backgrounds or anything like that. it was just a feeling i had.

i sat between a talent and a dreamer.

the talent designed detailed pendant jewelry then crafted it from silver or copper.

the dreamer was really a writer. she claimed it was a hobby, but you could see traces of text on her forearm, down the side of her neck. not actual faded markings—she didn't write on herself, but her body, her mind was the attaché she carried at all times, and if you asked her certain questions her skin would glow and words would float on the surface like lily pads.

her common tagline was, 'i write stories. i'm not a writer.' i thought of her as a dreamer because the way she listened to other people speak was similar to how people look when they fall in love.

i sat at the communal table, between the talent and the dreamer, and revealed a passion of mine. the one most likely to receive affirmations and the familiar round of questions. i told them i played the cello.

> [*as if answering the series of questions from around the table*]

my mother taught me from the time i was two and a half until the week before i left for college.
her father started teaching her when she was three.
he got the one scholarship they offered to a negro child for further study at a local music academy. he started playing in grade school.
i don't play professionally. never want to. it's just something i like to do.

by then the food came from the kitchen, thank god, and it tasted as good as the head chef sounded. a cornmeal recipe from a southern country was paired with a cabbage appetizer from out east. beef was broiled in a northern tradition and beans were mashed western style. the spices in each dish tasted like a private, personal destiny. we cleaned the plates as quickly as they arrived and as the food filled our empty stomachs our conversation embraced a fusion of distant intimacy. people shared emotional memories as if they were dry historical facts, but we all felt we needed to leave parts of our selves to make room for this delicious food inside of us.

it's crazy how food can demand such loyalty and even crazier that we supplied it. without question or hesitation.
the funny thing is we purged chunks of our personal history, thinking it was best for the meal, and totally downplayed, even dismissed, the power

our narratives held. we left them in the center of the table as if they were toothpicks, and everyone grabbed somebody else's and picked the remaining shards of food from in between our teeth.

the abstract painter sitting across from me told us she let some old, white state trooper with a horse-shoe-shaped bald pattern go down on her to avoid the speeding ticket that would get her license revoked.

the dancer sitting next to her told us his parents intentionally gave him and his brother 'racially ambiguous names' to better the chances of getting a foot in the doorway of opportunity.

i considered what it meant to say what i wanted to say to these five brown bodies, but i shoved the thought aside only to have the doubt reappear just before i spoke. i ended up altering my tale slightly, changing a few conjunctions and one or two verbs. the story had only shades of my true self in it. i felt spared but also felt like a coward. i refused a particular bond with these people and for what? it wasn't like i would ever see any of them again. right …?

after everyone shared, we all sat back in our seats, instantly stricken with the -itis. the metaphorical button had been undone on our collective dress pants.

the bill arrived as the dreamer pointed out the racial thread that lived in each of our stories. apparently, none of us offered 'neutral' memories— her word choice, not mine. the singer at the table, (that made six of us: the writer, the jewelry maker, the cello player (me!), the abstract painter, the dancer, and the singer) she took issue with the word 'neutral' as soon as the dreamer dropped it.

'what, exactly, is 'neutral' about being a person of color in this country?'

and right before my eyes the dreamer transformed into the realist, 'maybe if more brown folks stopped playing defense and just went about their lives, we'd have fewer race driven narratives. events would unfold and exist as pure circumstance, not discrimination.'

umm, what?!—are you serious?—that is totally ridiculous!—but what if the circumstance is pure discrimination?—she can't be—but what about —you—that—no—it isn't—[*resorts to sounds*]—ub—ugh—ahhh—ack— psssshhhhhhhhhh!!!

i returned to my day job. paralegal.
an office job housed in the type of office building that tourists took pictures of.
the glass and metal façade caught every sunset with awe-inspiring grace.
you can buy postcards of the sunlight hitting that building.

i returned to my day job in that office building where i sorted legal documents, labeled folders, put the docs in the folder then put the folder in a cardboard box that was not a racecar.
long hours. okay pay. mindless tasks. lots of paper cuts—little ones & big ones.
the writer, nicknamed dreamer, turned realist kept entering my thoughts.

her belief that events could unfold as pure circumstance sounded simple.
neutral narratives? logical possibility. but then i walked through the halls of that law firm, past the painted portraits of dead partners, long gone founders, angular, middle-aged white men in three-piece suits casually holding a briar tobacco pipe or wire reading glasses. then i talked to the smooth faced, dark-skinned man, who worked in the mailroom for 42 years. the day before his retirement he carved his name and years of service into the back wall of the stock room.

did the retired mailroom manager have a 'neutral' narrative?

he showed me the makeshift monument, filled with the names of Black folks who had retired before him. i took in those letters, the numbers and it felt like a luxury of the young and educated to come up with theoretical terms to apply to real experiences and struggles. to add one's name to the company of others speaks of a narrative swollen with opinion, shaded with color. there was nothing 'neutral' about that action. right? in a single etching those people told a truth: i was here.

was the mail room memorial equal to that of the portraits of the founding partners? both groups cemented their existence in that building. the mailroom manager carved his name using his pocketknife. the founding

partner commissioned the work from an established artist. is their legacy in the building equal? neutral? should it be?

i rode the Q13 to and from work, carrying these thoughts with me. i began studying the faces that surrounded me every morning, every evening. the book i was reading at the time remained in my bag. the music i listened to grew softer and softer with each trip until i finally turned it off, removed the earbuds.

i was looking for that face, listening for that voice that held no affect. that person of color who denounced —isms, or didn't care one way or the other about –isms, straight up like 'whatever'—but that's the thing, it wasn't about feigning disinterest. it wasn't about being the teflon don of oppression. (and the ones with the trodden souls didn't count because their neutrality came from defeat, like an eraser rubbing and rubbing away until it disappeared.) i wanted that golden face. that pure brown soul. that pitch perfect voice in the key of C. man or woman, boy or girl, i wanted to capture it, press it between two slides, and look at it through a microscope.

but see, the thing about change is that it can … well, it can change the rules at any given moment. it can shuffle the deck of cards you were using to hustle your way from day to day. it can just really fuck some shit up. especially if it starts at the inside. if it starts at the core, the base of your thinking then seeps its way through your system. if you can look like nothing's going down, all the while there's chaos going on deep in you, that's where the trouble is. because your friends can't say, 'hey, are you alright? you don't look so good.' they won't say that because you look fine, maybe even better than you looked in a long while. your friends will want to know what your secret is, but you can't tell them it's self-

defeating. you can't tell them it's uncertainty. you can't tell them you were
looking for a person of color with no color to tell you neutral narratives.
yea .... no, you can't tell them that.
so, i said: been going to the gym.
drinking mango smoothies.
using organic shampoo.
homemade teeth whitener.
sauna.
meditation.
more sleep.
less thinking.
stopped thinking. about it.
just stopped thinking about it.
chose to rub my quests inside my hands.
chose to pick up my cello and play and play and ...

> [*quietly recites a piece of music, but instead
> of singing the melody she names the notes and
> rests. if it's a four count she says the name of
> the note for four counts. this goes on for a long
> while. should become hypnotic. to her ears
> she's playing a lovely piece of music.*]

time dances for me when i play.

> [*recites the names of notes, rests softly…*]

the soil pushes orchids closer to the sun.

> [*recites in hushed breaths*]

my expectations recede.

> [*recites…*]

Things changed at my day job
when an office became vacant on the 23rd floor.

and my supervisor put in a request for another document room.
and i asked him if i could sit in that room.
Things changed when i got a window.
a metal desk.
a simple black chair on four wheels. no armrests.
a phone.
a computer.
and 100, 000 pages of discovery documents.

i printed two pictures i found online.
one was a picture of a beach. the other was a map.
i taped both pictures to the back of the door.
the beach was just under the coat hook.
the map was just above the doorknob.

those 100,000 pages were documents from the opposing side.
documents i had to sort, label and stuff in folders.
my hours doubled.
i had help but worked by myself in my office.
the sun rose.
the sun set.
i sorted, labeled, stuffed.
and for what?
$17/hr plus time and a half.

100-hour work weeks.
i billed the two hours i slept.
the meals were free.
there was a shower on the 15th floor.
sorted, labeled, stuffed.
coffee. diet coke. red bull. ice water. jumping jacks. mountain dew.
those paper cuts you can't see but you can feel—they hurt the most.
usually got the giggles around 345am.
at 530 i studied the map.
wheeled myself to the door and looked at that map.
a way out?
or a way in?
the bedolina map.

a little over 4,000 years old.
engraved on a rock in italy.
13 feet long. 7 feet wide.
but on the back of my door the picture is the size of my hand.

> [*she holds up her hand. she studies her hand*]

a way out, or a way in?
a prehistoric representation of a land.
rectangles, points, circles, single lines that lead you.
a series of figures, chiseled into stone, tried to tell us how to get from
where we were to where we oughta be.
i studied that map.
i climbed inside the picture, stepped carefully onto its earth. inhaled so
deep that my lungs creaked.

the air was different. it had a taste that spread across my tongue, played
with every bud. sweet, then sour, then spicy, then cold. i looked at the
space around me. what i saw floated in tears. my sight was blurry. i wiped
the wet away. my eyes adjusted to the elements. the grass was greener.
plush. the soft back of a doting mother. a flock of birds called to me from
behind, above. my feet slipped against the dew. i turned to speak to them,
but i lost my slipping grip and on a downward slope i slid. my body
pricked the land. rocks and twigs and bugs bruised my skin, broke its
barrier, tasted my blood. i tumbled at gravity's mercy. the blue sky, white
clouds thrusted against flashes of dark soil to create a baby so unique
that it could've been chosen to represent the most popular sugar brand in
the world. i rolled and flopped and tossed against the sliding slope until i
landed in the oglio river. the water's chill shook me like a bad habit.
soaked my casual business attire. the crease in my black pants—ruined.
my button-down shirt torn. my updo fell down, limp. i tasted metal. a
shadow cooled me from the sun. i looked up to see a man. his presence
frightened me but made me happy to see another pair of eyes, another
nose attached to a face, connected to a neck that joined a body tanned by
the yellow sun. he held in his hand a long, narrow bronze object. he held
it above his head then swiftly slammed it against mine.

my simple black chair on four wheels rolled my brown body back to my metal desk.

the map was torn in half. lines broken. circles divided.

Things stayed the same at my day job.

That changed the night i finally got a chance to go home. to sleep in my own bed.

that changed.

the night i climbed onto the Q13. sat in the back and fell right to sleep.

i missed my stop.

i woke up at the end of the line. the doors opened and the cross breeze, the fall night air, sat against my face.

i opened my eyes to see the city lights. their reflection rolled in the black water of the pier.

a flock of passengers filed off the Q13 to board the ferry.

i was too tired to get upset.

too wiped to beat myself up.

the next Q13 departed in 23 minutes.

i counted the seconds.

as time ticked slowly to the tock, i realized that it had been months since i'd gone anywhere other than my apartment or the firm.

months since my fusion lunch with those creative brown souls.

months since i became obsessed with neutral narratives falling from colored lips.

why was i counting 23 minutes when i had given up so many days and weeks?

my anger jump started the bus. it set out on its route, heading back the way it came.

halfway through my return trip the abstract painter who sat at the table of my fusion experience stepped on board.

she remembered me.

i remembered her: the traffic cop. his bald spot. her pussy. scott free.

that fall night on that Q13 ride across town she was an inspiring cliché. dried paint splattered on her khakis and her scuffed work boots. the streaks on her clothes told me she preferred vibrant colors, deep and rich, startling enough to make the mouth water. markers and pencils poked out from her tote that had a sketch of an african baobab tree printed on the front. she spoke in long strokes, laughed easily. she carried the blessings of o'keefe, basquiat, in her palms, on the back of her wrists.

she invited me to a party that was happening saturday night. i said yes.

the throw down was a get down in a hyped-up way. beautiful bronze bodies draped in limited edition clothes walked around in 3-figure sneakers, hand-crafted loafers, teetering heels. the abstract painter was my accessory, so i didn't feel out of place. she kept me with her even as several people tried to pull her away to talk with this brother who designed 'blah' or the sista who's stylin the new 'so&so' video. i went where she went. watched her talk, listened to the words exchanged. when anyone asked i told them i was a musician. they lost interest when i told them what instrument i played. there was an open bar sponsored by an expensive vodka brand so the room spun with the energy of a wind up toy. i didn't drink and neither did the painter, but a second-hand buzz caught both of us and the dj played some banging joints that made even the elitist Black kids sing along.

> [*goes into a rhyme to the beat and lyrical style
> of kanye west's song "flashing lights"*]

the get down got lower still / when the / lights changed and the bodies spilled / on the / dance floor / nobody was schmoozing no more / the dj was playing dem songs / i longed for the chance / to settle in the cut of a trance / with the mind of my choosing,/ but i used 'em, picked 'em up, dropped 'em back down then switched 'em up. / i'm just playing / but back to what i was saying / about them cool black kids, / dripping in ivy, hbc's, brunch everyday, and copping the latest steez. / the room was swole but i was slim, / just taking it all in. / i wished they were my reflection / even if my attitude looked like rejection. / the painter asked if i was okay. / i said maybe so, in my own way. / you want some air? / that would be fair / since i'm bringing the party down./ she frowned then took my hand, / we crossed the dance floor, climbed up the stairs. / opened the door, / the night seemed colder than before / behind us the metal door slammed.

we stood on the roof.

we didn't talk for a long while.
the view from up there hushed all words.
my thoughts swung from her to the idea of myself.
she painted abstractly, i lived my days in the same way.
the bass from the party thumped beneath us.
she spoke first.
i responded.
our conversation wasn't an easy one, but something about the moment
felt effortless.
her phrases were coated in clear intentions, which helped ease the
anxiety i collected from watching the crowd dance downstairs.
i spoke.
she responded.
the gold jewelry she wore made me think of butterscotch. the night
smelled of licorice.
she asked if i would play my cello in her studio.
i said yes.
she asked if i would watch her paint.
i said yes.

what was she working on?
she told me she had become obsessed with depicting neutral narratives,
capturing the concept of pure circumstance on a two-dimensional plane.
i was thrilled that she was swept up in the same maze i was, consistently
arriving at dead ends but never losing motivation to find it. i could've
flown into the black sky.

but instead, i asked when was a good time to visit her space.

the puddle jumper airplane is included in my unlimited access to the
city's transportation. my trip to her studio was the first time i rode in one.
warehouses, factories, silos, and the field of 40-feet tall solar powered
windmills inhabit a strip of land adjacent to the city. no one works in
those buildings anymore. popeye-esque laborers were pushed out of that

area to be replaced by creative types. The types who're looking for inexpensive housing and a community of like-minded potheads to spin trip-hop records and read 18th century poetry.

her studio got amazing sunlight. streams of natural light that fostered a need to create beauty. the light demanded a muse to shine on, and she supplied it. huge pieces that held you close. shapes and colors and shades earned your trust, earned a nook in the deepest part of your realest self.

she entertained there. worked there. slept there.

my cello, in its bright orange case, settled into that environment easier than i did.
i felt tense in the arms of her creativity. tense or insecure or overwhelmed.

i couldn't figure out which or if it was all those things.

she turned to take out the pieces that were inspired by that lunch.
pure circumstance.
neutral narrative.

they were small, much smaller than her other works. the size of a book of sacred text. i held out my hands and she placed sheet after sheet of un-stretched canvas on top. it was as if the size communicated an uncertainty in her endeavor.

they
were
wrong.
everything about all of them were wrong.
or.
or.
they didn't speak to me the way i needed them to.

she picked up on my disappointment.
'i have to keep trying,' is all she said as she removed the final one from my hands.

during my trip home, as i rode the puddle jumper back, i watched the city from above. the picture gradually changed from warehouses to grey, choppy waters, to office buildings, to a chilly landing strip. locations shifted from moment to moment, but what i saw remained constant: doubt. those paintings were supposed to show me the neutral, but they confirmed the –isms. as i rode the Q13 to my apartment, uncertainty pressed against my morale. what if the neutral wasn't meant to be found? what if it existed in the negative spaces? on the brink of possibility, but never in clear sight? maybe that person of color with no color isn't even meant to be seen. and even if i did see them, would they have anything to say? maybe there's no neutral narrative worth telling. or worth listening to. what if the neutral was boring? or ignorant? had funky breath? or a stank attitude?

these questions bummed me out. in a real way. in a surprising way. i realized part of me wanted to find out if this person was happy. maybe the neutral narrative could be a happy one. a tale void of struggle, full of satisfaction. that person of color with no color may be living a life filled with yes-es and "of course you can".

that's a possibility, too. right?
that night, i fell asleep in the arms of blind motivation.
my quest for the neutral remained.
the following day, I took a roundabout way to work.
my 20-minute commute grew into 37 minutes.
the day after that, 37 became 53 minutes.
the conflict popped off when i didn't allow the extra time i needed to make it to work at a reasonable hour.

my supervisor liked me and my lateness caused more concern than anger. we sat in his office when he asked if everything was okay. that question felt like a stupid one. but his tone was so sincere.

i looked at him: a sadness held his face together like super glue. his red hair had flecks of blonde that shined like a golden ticket. his skin was

smooth, a patch of faint freckles straddled his nose. i sat in his office and wondered: did this white boy have a neutral narrative?

i offered to buy him a drink. he accepted.

the pub was located on a side street not far from the firm.

he held the door open for me, helped me remove my coat, pulled out my chair.

people get curious when a white boy enters a room with a black girl. get real curious when that white boy is chivalrous. side glances, straight up

looks, and a comment or two were exchanged between table mates. every gesture was slight, but the room was curious nonetheless.

he changed his mind about drinking alcohol.
i did too.
he had soda.
i had juice.

he let me lead the conversation. i asked him if he noticed the looks when we walked in. he said he did. i asked how he felt about it. he said people are jerks. asked me how i felt about it. people are jerks, i echoed. his response was discouraging. i steered us into the shallow end of discussion topics. i didn't get a refill on my juice. he finished his mountain dew. we went back outside. he hesitated just as we parted ways, asked me 'are you sure you're ok.' the weather changed. the sun left its post and settled beneath the city. my supervisor looked less like a supervisor in the dusk. i saw a different face in the evening light. i trusted this face more than before. 'i'm not. i'm not ok. my body is fine, but my spirit is …' i ran out of adjectives.

my bed was hot that night. so hot that i laid there naked, but still felt i had on my work clothes—a dark wool suit and scoop neck blouse. gold studs in my earlobes. but i only had on my skin, my thoughts, my breath, my pulse. all these things were supposed to be weightless. the blackness of night, of skin, of truth muscled its way into my tiny apartment, sucked out the dignity, the faith that i worked so hard to fashion into a noose and slide around my neck. wait—scratch that. no. nothing about nooses. *gurl what's wrong with you?!* scratch that. it's just heat. ain't the end of the world. no apocalyptic dives into the well of armageddon, ms. thing. drink some ice water. everything is fine. just play …. just play … and play … and …

[*quietly recites the notes from a piece of music*]

i sat in the living room, in the darkness, in my nakedness and played music.
my brown skin melted into the cello's hue.
i cooled off as my tone coiled around its timbre.
i slept on a minor key that night.

the following morning, i called in to work and took a personal day.

i was convinced i had to break away from my work commute and walk the city. it was clear, at that point, that whoever i was looking for didn't frequent the Q13 bus, my neighborhood or the office building where i worked. i decided that morning as i crawled out of bed as i sat on the toilet as i stood in the shower—i decided that day would be the day i

would find a person of color whose narrative isn't tethered to their race or gender. a person of color with a neutral narrative.

but what would this somebody sound like? look like? she could be any race, any ethnicity. he could speak in a range of inflections, a particular cadence. i just wanted to talk to that somebody who didn't carry any – isms. all i needed was an identity, a narrative that was unconcerned, uncommitted, unaffected.

the sun started to rise as i stepped out of my apartment building. i flagged down a moto'bike and told him to take me to the junction overpass. we arrived at the destination safe and sound. and as i dismounted the back of

his bike i said thank you and told him to have a good day. he responded with such a weighted purpose i knew he had chiseled his narrative into a specific shape, stained it the same tint as his olive-colored skin. a sticker of a country's flag had been applied to the right side of his helmet. i asked if he was from there. he said, 'i was born there but grew up here'. he asked me had i been there. i told him no, but asked 'what is it like?' he said he hadn't been back since he was a baby. he only knew his neighborhood's version of his home country. he nodded farewell and zoomed away. i stood there for a moment and thought about what he said. considered the stitching that joined culture to race, ethnicity to culture. if i found the somebody with a neutral tale what would their cultural identity be? would they have ties to particular customs? could the neutral have a culture? could a culture be neutral?

i looked up at the landscape before me.
i started my walk as the sun continued her climb towards the center of the sky.

> [*she uses her hand as a map of the city. points out her route*]

[*the tip of her middle finger*] i began in the neo-factory district. workers from all over the city entered square brick buildings to assemble refrigerator motors, bake tortillas, restore antiques. i moved against the current of laborers trying to catch blank eyes in a sea of faces, but everyone presented a detailed racial identity. every face held a sided truth, every morning greeting had a distinct melody.

i kept walking.

> [*the lower section of her index finger*]

At the public art gardens, i met an old cinnamon-hued gentlemen who recounted for me his puerto-congolese neighborhood's history of white flight. i heard his tale, saw his truth. nothing was neutral about his identity. he finished his lesson then asked where my people were from. i told him the south to which he inquired, 'the south of <u>what</u>?' i said the name of the place i <u>wanted</u> my people to come from. he smiled as if i had complimented his blue eyes then offered me a piece of candy. the wrapper was bright with cartoonish letters printed all over it. i accepted it, slipping it into my pocket. a treat for later.

i walked.

in the urban suburbia section of the city, i talked to a group of new
moms. a crew of hindu-talians each bouncing an offspring on one knee.

one woman remained quiet during the entire exchange. her focus was
held tight on her daughter, a plump bundle with cherry molasses skin
and curly

hair that was dark with sporadic flashes of blonde. the baby started to
fuss and her mother began to quietly hum a song, holding the child close
in order to feel the vibrations that occurred with each note. we all grew
silent in the presence of the melody. lyrics appeared here and there, but
they were delivered in a language that was foreign to me. i learned from
the leader of the pack that the lullaby was first sung by their maternal
ancestors. passed down from mother to daughter for generations.

*[she listens. quietly collects and names the notes.
it's a beautiful melody to her ear]*

as i parted ways with them, they offered cultural blessings and well
wishes for my future children and my children's children.

i walked.

*[on her hand she points to the same location as
previous, but travels south arriving at the first
dark line in her palm]*

i bought a pack of cigarettes and started conversations in the smoker
sections outside of the hospital,

[points out another spot slightly to the west]

the courthouse

[slightly further south]

the dmv.

i walked.

chats at the jesuit technical college. the local organic food bank.

i walked.

racially distinct narratives stuck to my clothes, my skin.

i walked.

the west side library. the outlet mall.

i gathered narratives but each one was swayed by race and gender. i asked origin of birth 150 times. neighborhood of residence 198 times. i shook 205 brown hands. each set of eyes—green, brown, grey, blue— assumed a connection with me. but i gracefully avoided any questions that would've confirmed a bond. i was growing discouraged. i hadn't found what i was looking for. i saw a shade of color, a thread of culture in each person of color i talked to.

i was here [*points at the base of her thumb*] as the sun started its retreat into the horizon. i sat by a fountain and watched a group of young black boys do tricks on skateboards. my feet ached. i retrieved the piece of candy that the old puerto-congolese man gave me. the words on the wrapper had a few things in common with my own language, but just enough of it was unfamiliar. i could decipher the words "sweet" and "breath." the wrapper was a vibrant shade of pink with bursts of purple on both of the twisted ends. it looked so saturated and felt so soft against my fingertips, i wondered if it were edible, too. i touched it with the tip of my tongue. [*twisted face*] not meant to be eaten. [*face relaxes*]

i removed the wrapping to reveal a round piece of candy that was bright, bold unaffected. i looked at it, realizing it had been hours since i had paid attention to anything so … vacant. i let the ball of candy roll around in my palm watching its shape remain constant, its hue remain unaltered. it smelled a bit like guava with a pinch of mint. i put it in my mouth, felt it give under the pressure of my teeth. i chewed and chewed and chewed. it turned out to be gum. breath refreshing chewing gum.

i heard the laughter of a child close by. i turned to face the sound and saw an older man teach his son how to make a wish in the fountain. they each tossed a coin into the water and watched it sink to the bottom. i looked into the water, not expecting to see my own reflection.

i saw no color, no shade, no hue.

i touched my face. my brow relaxed. i watched my hand smooth out my hair. it … it was as if i had forgotten how to see myself.

quietly, privately i began a conversation with this woman. this self. i asked the reflection,

'what's your name?'

but there was no response.

'where are you from?'

no response.

'who are your people?'

the reflection replied, 'my mother, my daddy, my grandpa.'

'what do you do?'

the reflection quivered in the breeze. no response.

'what is your name?'

no response.

i asked myself these questions but could not provide any answers.

yet the narratives i collected throughout the day rang fresh in my mind. i could tell you every story from every person i talked to that day, but my own narrative, the details of my substance had grown foreign to me.

i stepped away from the water erasing my portrait.

i turned to take in the scenery around me.
disoriented.

the evening rush hour began and i pushed my way into the center of the current of white-collar workers as they migrated onto the downtown ferry. i took the first empty seat i saw.

i felt a disfigured exhilaration.
i had finally discovered that person of color with no color but lost my own narrative as a consequence. i was that piece of chewing gum, unaffected although surrounded by a shifting palm.

change never arrives by itself.
before & after disorientation elation loneliness.
my hollow roots began to crack with each question that rang inside of me. i got up from the seat and pushed my way onto the deck.
the night air filled my empty skin. goose bumps.

i leaned against the rusting yellow rail and watched the water dance under the moonlight unable to find any answers in the blackness ...
i remain this way, relieved that my quest has been conquered, but desperate to recall a piece of my own narrative. i remember ... i ... play the cello. i remember jolly rancher glasses ... cardboard boxes ... [*names a series of notes*]... mother ... father .... anything more beyond that lunch with the five brown bodies at the family style restaurant is unknown to me.

i can only recall my obsession with the neutral.

i sit with you, victorious, but ... but what is my name?

where am i from?

who do i think i am? who could i be?

[she turns to someone in the audience seated closest to her]

tell me.

who are my people?

[she turns to another person]

where do you think i'm from?

who do you think i am?

what do you think my story could be?

lights fade to black.

Christina Anderson is a Tony nominated playwright, screenwriter, educator, and creative. Plays include: *the ripple, the wave that carried me home, How To Catch Creation, pen/man/ship, Man In Love, The Ashes Under Gait City, BlackTop Sky,* and *Good Goods.* Her work has appeared at The Goodman Theatre, OSF, The Public Theatre, Yale Repertory Theatre, Kansas City Rep, and other theaters in the United States and Canada. Awards and honors include: 2021 Prince Prize, 2020 United States Artists Fellow, MacDowell Fellowship, Lily Awards Harper Lee Prize, Herb Alpert Award nomination, Barrymore Nomination, and New Dramatists Residency.

tripwireharlot.com

Made in United States
Troutdale, OR
12/16/2023